P9-DBS-064

PUZZLES PARADOXES AND BRAIN TEASERS

No. 2895
$14.95

PUZZLES PARADOXES AND BRAIN TEASERS

STAN GIBILISCO

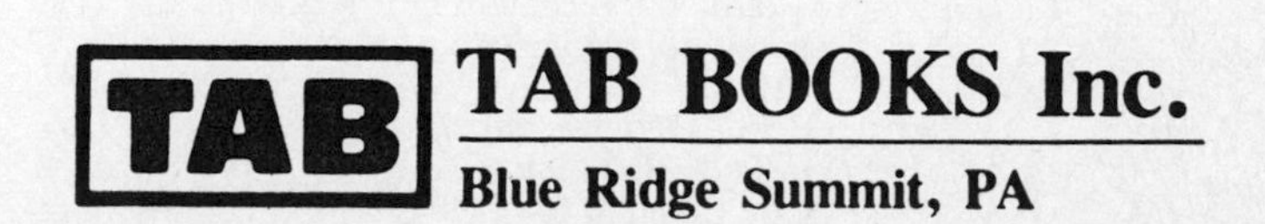

FIRST EDITION
FIRST PRINTING

Printed in the United States of America

Library of Congress Cataloging in Publication Data

Gibilisco, Stan.
Puzzles, paradoxes, and brain teasers / Stan Gibilisco.
p. cm.
Includes index.
ISBN 0-8306-7895-6 ISBN 0-8306-2895-9 (pbk.)
1. Mathematical recreations. I. Title.
QA95.G48 1987
793.7'4—dc 19 87-29053
CIP

Questions regarding the content of this book
should be addressed to:

Reader Inquiry Branch
TAB BOOKS Inc.
Blue Ridge Summit, PA 17294-0214

Contents

Introduction

OUR PHYSICAL WORLD IS IMPERFECT; WE ALL concede that. Things don't always work out just the way we want them to. Bank checks bounce when they shouldn't; strange and unexplainable things happen. People tell lies and we don't know whom to believe. Dust accumulates on furniture. It can be a frustrating place to live, sometimes, and it is fun now and then to escape from the imperfect physical world into some perfect world. Some of us do this by means of games such as chess or various video games or board games. We all need an escape. Mathematics provides an escape for some, into a world that is supposedly perfect. But is it?

The logician, Bertrand Russell, was one of the first to shake the very foundations of this supposedly perfect universe, the basis for all knowledge, as it has been called. He pointed out that certain very simple propositions, all intuitively plausible, would result in a contradiction. This caused an uproar in the whole field of mathematics. Such a contradictory result, arising from sound assumptions, is called a *paradox*. We can also include under this category those things that work when it would appear they could not possibly work. An example of this is finding the slope of a curve at a certain point.

Mathematical puzzles, brain teasers, and paradoxes are too frustrating for some people to even think about. It bothers them. Others, perhaps you, get a kick out of it. It's sort of like laughing in the face of a cosmos that thinks it's perfect, after you have taken its very foundations and shown that it isn't.

In this book, we will examine some common mathematical puzzles—games that we can play that have solutions that are not obvious but, when we find out what they are, we laugh at ourselves for missing anything so simple.

We will look at the foundation of mathematics, and therefore perhaps the foundation of all thinking: logic. We will see how commonly accepted logic operates and examine some of the paradoxes that arise in this field.

One of the more interesting brain teasers in the mathematical world is the concept of upper bounds and lower bounds. The concept is especially intriguing because it relates directly to the physical world. How fast, for example, will a person ever be able to swim the 100-meter freestyle? Some would say there is no limit, but there has to be. It's got to be more than one second, for example. Mathematically, if there is a lower bound, such as one second, then there is a greatest lower bound—an exact limiting time for how fast the 100-meter freestyle can be swum. We will look at the theory behind this odd phenomenon of mathematics and see some examples.

There are various different fields in mathematics, all containing their own paradoxical or brain-teasing aspects. We will look at some of these aspects of mathematics and see the sorts of strange things that arise.

Another fascinating paradox arises out of one of the most commonly accepted theories in science today: the theory of relativity. It has been found by experiments verifying Einstein's predictions that time in fact "slows down" as speed increases. But this results in a paradox that implies that two people, the same age at the outset of a journey, can end up at different ages at the end. Not only this, but one is older than the other at the same time the other is older than the one!

The concept of "infinity" has intrigued mathematicians for centuries. There are various ways this idea can be conceived. The most commonly accepted today is the Cantorian concept of transfinite cardinal numbers. At first his theory was ridiculed by his colleagues. (It is said he died insane, perhaps from the deriding he got.) We will look at a less common concept of infinity—the idea of division by zero. This idea contains an inherent contradiction, a paradox, as does the whole chapter. Can you find it?

Paradoxes in mathematics affect the physical world also. In the last chapter, we will examine some of these anomalies in our real universe.

It is hoped that you'll get some enjoyment out of this book, and not just frustration; paradoxes are annoying, it is true, but perhaps without them, our world would be nothing but a singularity, a point with no height, width, depth, or duration. That would be terrible, wouldn't it?

Well, that, too, is possible!

Chapter 1

Puzzles and Paradoxes

THE WORLD OF MATHEMATICS ABOUNDS WITH problems that seem to defy solution, only to have answers that are counter-intuitive or so obvious (once we know the solution) that we feel like kicking ourselves for being so blind. This is especially true of "prove-it" problems, but can be shown in countless other situations. These kinds of puzzles and paradoxes irritate some people and entertain others. Those who long for perfect order and precision in this universe are likely to be frustrated no matter where they go, and this is no less true in mathematics, the supposedly perfect science, than in any other endeavor. For those who enjoy contemplating these imperfections in our universe —well, there are plenty of them to go around, and if you're one of these people, you won't be frustrated.

IRRATIONAL NUMBERS

The very word "irrational" stirs thoughts of madness, and the layman might be tempted to call a mathematician "mad" as he or she sits in an ivory tower pondering trivialities while the rest of us fight losing battles against taxes, pollution, job stress, and traffic jams. The image of the pipe-smoking, bearded mathematician on a university campus in the green forests of the Northeast, abstractedly spinning his gossamer equations high in an abstract sky but oblivious to everything else, is not altogether unfounded. Mathematics can be an escape from the banality of physical reality, and irrational numbers provide a perfect means to get away, and in these numbers, each one itself a string of numbers without end, the sequence entirely unpredictable, one can get a glimpse of infinity.

Irrational numbers are generally represented in their exact form if possible, because they cannot be entirely written out in decimal form. A common example of an irrational number is $\sqrt{2}$. This is the number we multiply by itself to get 2. If you try to write this number out in decimal form we will find that the sequence of digits does not end, and yet there is no apparent pattern of repetition. The geometric construction of $\sqrt{2}$ is easy; all we need to do is draw the diagonal of a square of 1 unit on a side (Fig. 1-1). This can be accomplished by means of the familiar rules of geometric construction using a straight edge and compass, yet putting this number in decimal form is impossible.

We are familiar with the repeating decimals, those whose digits do not come to an end yet can be predicted. An example of this is ⅓ = 0.33333 . . . . Another example is 24281/99999 = 0.2428124281 . . . . In either of these cases and in any known repeating-decimal situation, it is possible to find what the value of a certain digit in the sequence will be. But this is not the case, evidently, with an irrational number such as $\sqrt{2}$. Its decimal expansion is unpredictable.

This brings up the notion as to whether or not there truly is such a thing as a random number. It seems as if the digits in the decimal expansion of $\sqrt{2}$ occur unpredictably, and if this is in fact true, then the digits are in some sense "random." This seems to be the case with the decimal expansion of *any* irrational number. We have access to infinitely many irrational numbers; the square root of an integer is irrational if it is not an integer itself, for example. Hence we should have no problem finding random numbers for use in statistical analysis. But are these digits really random?

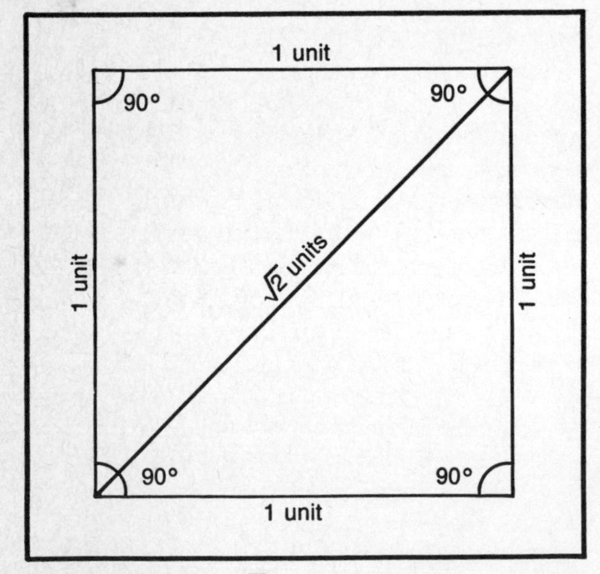

Fig. 1-1. The value of $\sqrt{2}$ can be geometrically constructed by drawing the diagonal of a square 1 unit on a side.

THE MEANING OF "RANDOM"

Generating a sequence of random numbers might at first appear to be easy. All we need to do, we might think, is rattle off digits from 0 to 9 in any ridiculous sequence we please, and the result will be a string of "random" numbers. But everyone has psychological hangups that make this method imperfect, or maybe we ought to say, not perfectly imperfect. Everyone will show a leaning or preference for certain digits or sequences of digits, such as 5 or 58. We would expect that, if a sequence of digits were truly random, the digit 5 would occur exactly one-tenth of the time, and the sequence of 58 exactly one-hundreth of the time for one-digit and two-digit sequences respectively. This is one of the necessary characteristics of randomness. Another is that of unpredictability; there should be absolutely no way of generating the next digit in a sequence of random digits—should there? If there is, the sequence couldn't be random because that next digit is predetermined—right?

It turns out that we can generate the value of $\sqrt{2}$ by means of a method called extracting square roots. This can be done for any integer, in fact. If we have the patience, and know the first n digits of a square root, we can find the n + 1st digit by means of this process. That puts a crimp on the idea that $\sqrt{2}$ has a decimal expansion with truly random digits. The same is true of other irrational numbers such as e and π that can be written in short form. (The number e is the natural logarithm base and π is the number of diameters in the circumference of a circle.) If the digits in an irrational number do not occur in random sequence, then, where can we find digits that do occur in truly random fashion?

Interestingly enough, it is possible that there is no such thing as a really random sequence of numbers if we require that the digits be unpredictable. If they are unpredictable then they cannot be generated by any algorithm, and this includes even the thought processes of the most jumbled-up human brain! Perhaps even the motion of molecules, atoms, protons, neutrons, and electrons, as well as all other atomic particles, can be predicted or precisely determined by some algorithm or mathematical formula. Then there is no such thing as perfect chaos in our universe, as well as no such thing as perfect order. At this point we get into a physical question, though, and have to quit the discussion; here we're concerned only with mathematics.

A BAND AROUND THE EARTH

We are all familiar with the irrational number pi (π), which is equal to approximately 3.1416 and represents the number of diameters in a circle (Fig. 1-2). This number has been known for thousands of years to be a constant that does not depend on the size of the circle as long as the measurements are made on a flat surface. The value of π also holds for the circumference versus the diameter of a sphere.

An interesting counter-intuitive result can be derived from simple application of the formula for the circumference of a circle or sphere to its diameter:

$$C = \pi d = 2\pi r$$

where C is the circumference, d is the diameter, and r is the radius, all in the same units. This has to do with the increase in size of a band around any circular (disk-shaped) or spherical object.

The puzzle goes something like this. Suppose the earth were a smooth, perfectly round sphere, with no hills or mountains. Imagine a rope around the earth's equator, strung so that it is snug and does not stretch. If we were to add, say, ten feet to this rope, and then prop it up all the way around the planet so that it stood out equally far everywhere, how far above the surface would it stand? We can assume the earth is 8,000 miles in diameter, and that one mile is 5,280 feet.

The answer may surprise you. Most people are inclined to think that the rope would stand out just a tiny, microscopic distance from the surface of the earth if ten feet were added to its length. The earth is huge by comparison to just ten feet of length: about 25,000 miles around, and ten feet is a miniscule fraction of that. But in fact the rope would stand out over a foot and a half.

Rather than get into calculations involving huge numbers such as how many feet are in the circumference of the earth, we can extend this assertion to claim that the rope would stand out the same distance no matter how large or small the planet was. The rope would stand out about a foot and a half if it were put around a basketball, the earth, or the sun. This is easy to prove.

Suppose the radius of the object in question is r feet. Then the circumference C is $2\pi r$, and the radius is $r = C/(2\pi)$. If we add ten feet to the circumference, the new radius r^* is given by

$$\begin{aligned} r^* = (C + 10)/(2\pi) &= C/(2\pi) + 10/(2\pi) \\ &= C/(2\pi) + 1.59 \end{aligned}$$

if we assume $\pi = 3.14$. But $C/(2\pi)$ is the original radius. So the radius grows by 1.59 feet, or about 19 inches, regardless of the radius. We call the radius r, and r might be anything—zero, three feet, a mile, 4,000 miles (the radius of the earth), or 432,000 miles (the radius of the sun). It might even be the radius of the whole galaxy, about 46,000 light years!

THIS STATEMENT IS FALSE

A common logical paradox is often cited in the self-contradicting assertion "This statement is

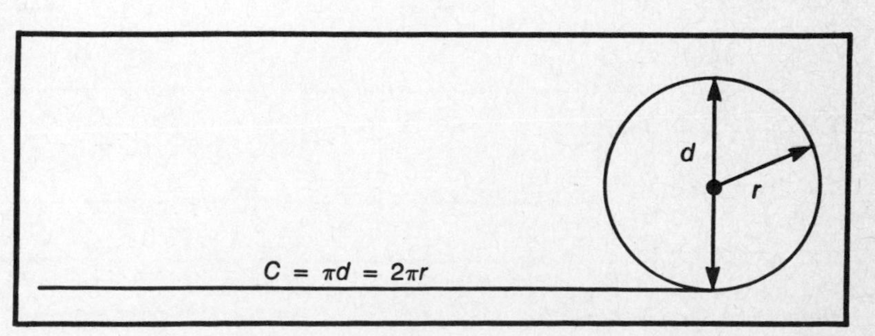

Fig. 1-2. The circumference of a circle is the diameter, d, multiplied by π, or twice the radius, r, multiplied by π. Here the circle rolls one revolution, marking out the circumference $C = \pi d = 2\pi r$.

false." If we believe it, then the statement is true, and this contradicts its assertion that it is false; if we don't believe it, then we assume it is false, but it's not true that it's false; therefore it's true. We can't win. A statement such as this is meaningless because it cannot be either true and cannot be false.

There are more complicated examples of logically meaningless groups of statements. The worst examples are entire mathematical theories that fall apart because they contain contradictions. Logicians have been haunted by the discovery, by Kurt Gödel in this century, that some logical systems will inevitably contain statements that cannot be proven nor disproven—that is, statements the truth value of which can't be determined.

Russell's Paradox is a more sophisticated example than the one given above. We can state this paradox like this. Suppose Sal is a barber in the town of Seville, and he shaves all barbers in the town who don't shave themselves. Sal shaves only these people, and no one else. Then does Sal shave himself, or not? You can figure out for yourself that a contradiction is reached whether you assume Sal shaves himself or not. If he shaves himself, he doesn't; if he doesn't, he does.

The peculiarities of mathematical logic, a large and complicated field in itself, will be discussed later. For now, you will have to be content to know that logic—the reasoning on which we base all of mathematics and indeed all of formal thought—is not as perfect as we might like to believe.

THE FROG AND THE WALL

A familiar problem in mathematics is the summing up of an infinite sequence in order to get a finite sum. The frog-and-wall paradox (or what at first seems to be a paradox) shows an example of this.

Suppose there is a frog at a certain distance from a wall, say, ten feet. Imagine that this frog jumps halfway to the wall, so that he is five feet away. Suppose he continues to jump toward the wall, each time getting halfway there. It is clear that he will never reach the wall, no matter how many times he jumps, and yet he has only ten feet to travel at the outset. The frog will die long before he gets to the wall, even though he almost reaches it (Fig. 1-3). No finite number of jumps will allow the frog to reach the wall; it will take an infinite

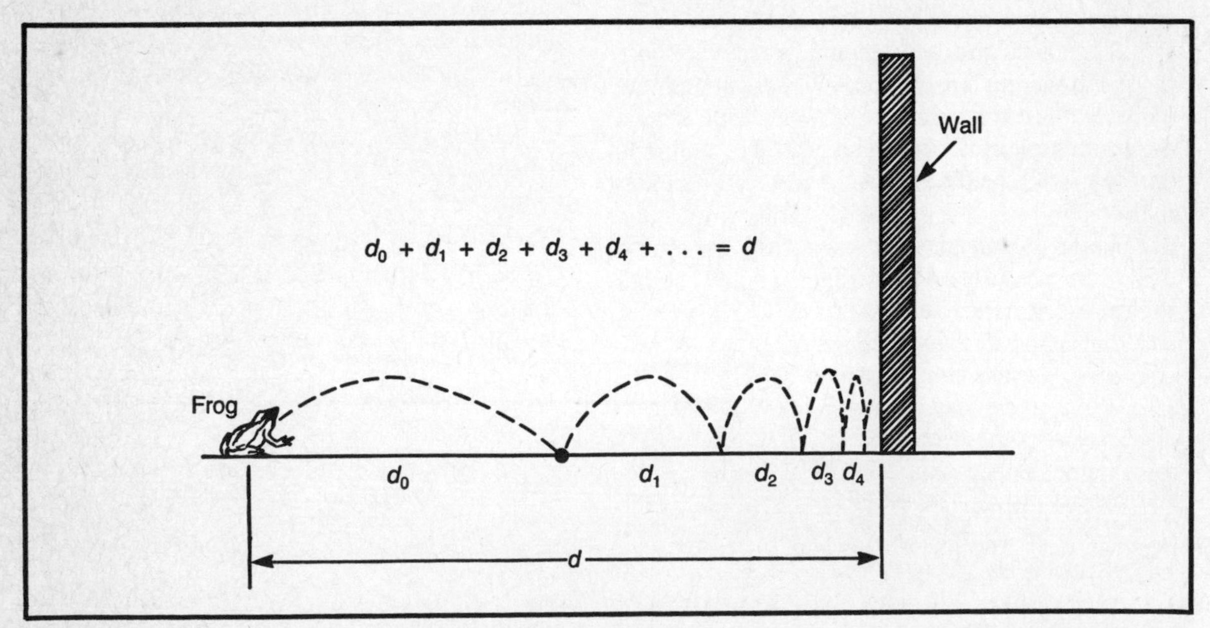

Fig. 1-3. A frog, jumping toward a wall and going halfway each time. The first distance traveled is d_0; the second is $d_1 = d_0/2$; the third is $d_2 = d_1/2$; and so on.

number of jumps. The mathematical series that this is based on is

$$\frac{1}{2} + \frac{1}{4} + \frac{1}{8} + \frac{1}{16} + \ldots = 1$$

If we keep cutting a number in half, over and over, and add the result, the final sum of the infinite series will be twice the original number. But we must add up an infinite number of numbers in order to get the exact sum; otherwise we can only approach the sum. In real life, of course, since there isn't time enough to add up an infinite number of numbers, we cannot obtain the final sum. The frog cannot reach the wall.

The same sort of argument can be used to prove that a hare, starting behind a tortoise in a race, will never reach the tortoise. Or, let's say, if you are driving at 55 miles per hour and trying to pass someone going only 50 miles per hour, you will never catch, let alone pass, your predecessor. How is this "proof" done? A simple model can be used. Figure 1-4 shows the geometric illustration.

The initial situation is shown at A; you, going 55 mph, are a certain distance d_0 behind the car you are trying to catch, going 50 mph. After a certain time you have traveled the distance d_0, and are in the position previously occupied by the other car. However, that car has now moved ahead by a distance d_1, so that it is in a new position. The distance d_1 is less than the distance d_0 by an amount that depends on d_0. The situation after you have traveled the distance d_0 is shown at B of Fig. 1-4.

Once you have traveled the distance d_1, the other car has moved ahead and is now in front of you by a distance d_2, as shown at C. The illustrations at D and E show what happens in the next two time frames, as you travel distance d_2 and then d_3. At E the car is ahead of you by distance d_4. This process goes on without end. Although $d_0 > d_1 > d_2 > d_3 > d_4 > \ldots$ is an endless sequence, you obviously will catch the slower car; you've doubtless done so in practice many times. But mathematically, you can't, according to this little demonstration. You must go through an infinite number of transitions in a finite amount of time, and this seems impossible.

The conclusion seems true—but isn't. The series $d_0 + d_1 + d_2 + d_3 + d_4 + \ldots$ is a convergent series. Its sum is finite, and the sum of the times $t_0 + t_1 + t_2 + t_3 + t_4 \ldots$ is also finite.

BRINGING INFINITY DOWN TO SIZE

The principle of a convergent series can be used to make infinity, or what we would like to call infinity, appear within reach. In the example of the 55-mph car passing the 50-mph car, we break down the process into an infinite number of little steps, all of which add up to one step, of finite distance, complete in a finite time. We can do the same thing with a coordinate system such as the familiar Cartesian plane (Fig. 1-5A). The Cartesian plane is simply a means of graphing one variable as a function of another, such as time versus temperature. The scale we choose for the axes of the plane is such that the range of variables is suitable for the purposes at hand. For example, we might choose hours for the time axis in a time-temperature graph, and degrees Celsius from 0 to 40 for the temperature axis. Or we might make one or both of the scales logarithmic to include a wider range or to produce a more meaningful-looking graph. Whatever scale we use, however, one thing is always true: the whole range of real numbers cannot be shown on one axis. Or can it? If we are willing to use the right kind of nonlinear scale, we can.

Figure 1-5B shows a coordinate plane in which the scales have been made according to the frog-and-wall series. For the range of real numbers greater than or equal to zero (the non-negative reals), we place the point 1 halfway between 0 and the end of the line; then 2 is halfway between 1 and the end; 3 is halfway between 2 and the end. In general, for a given integer n, the point for n is halfway between the point for $n - 1$ and the end. The end of the line is represented by either a point, in which case we can call it "infinity," or an open circle, in which case we don't define it at all. Either way, all of the real numbers are spoken for on this line segment of finite length, and we can easily prove this by showing that there is a one-to-one correspondence between the line segment (minus the end point at the right) and the real-number line. We

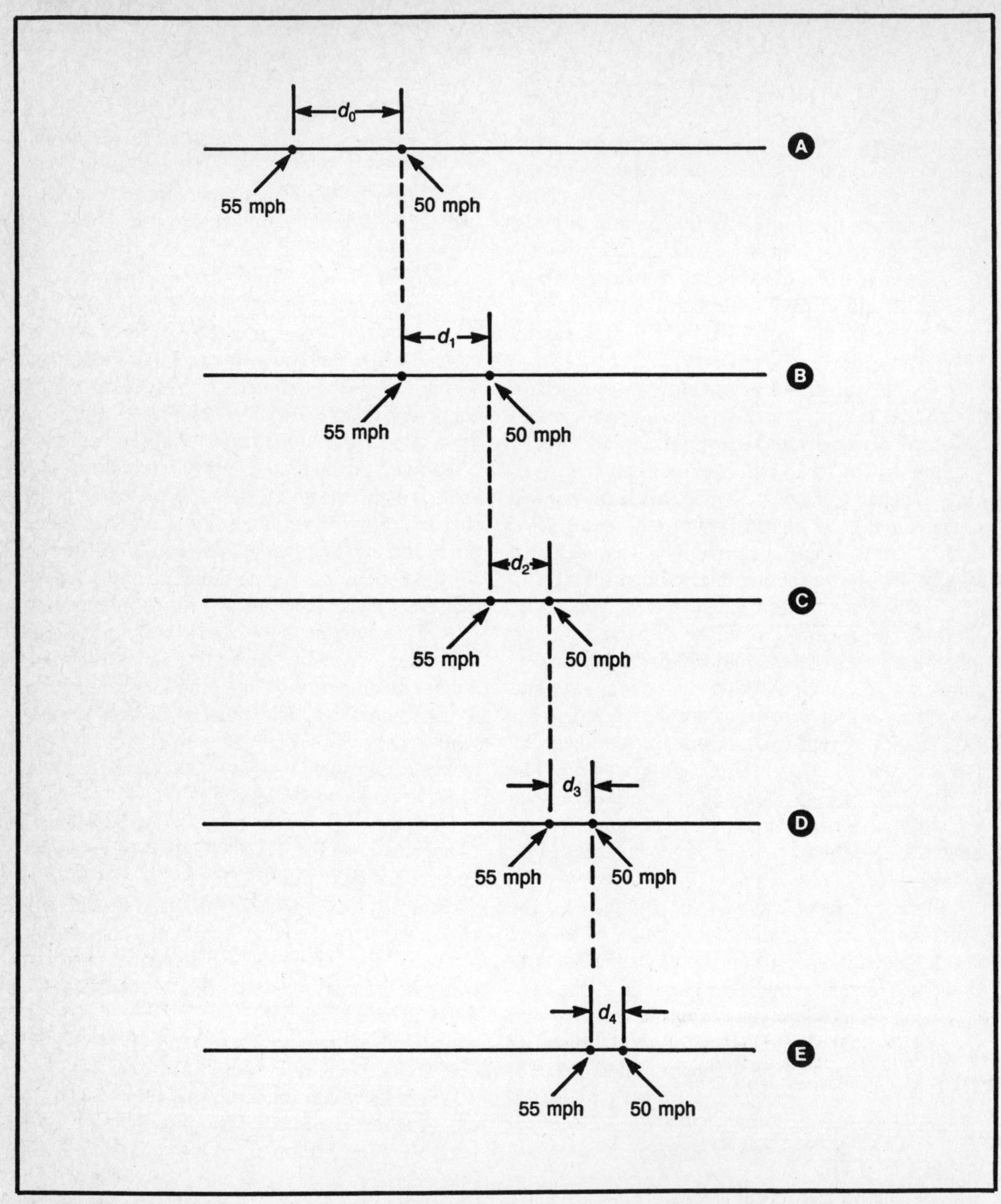

Fig. 1-4. A car going 55 mph catching a car going 50 mph. Distances d_1 through d_4 are discussed in the text. At A, the initial situation; at B, after the rear car has traveled distance d_0; at C, after the rear car has traveled $d_1 + d_0$; at D, after the rear car has gone $d_2 + d_1 + d_0$; at E, after the rear car has gone $d_3 + d_2 + d_1 + d_0$ from the initial point.

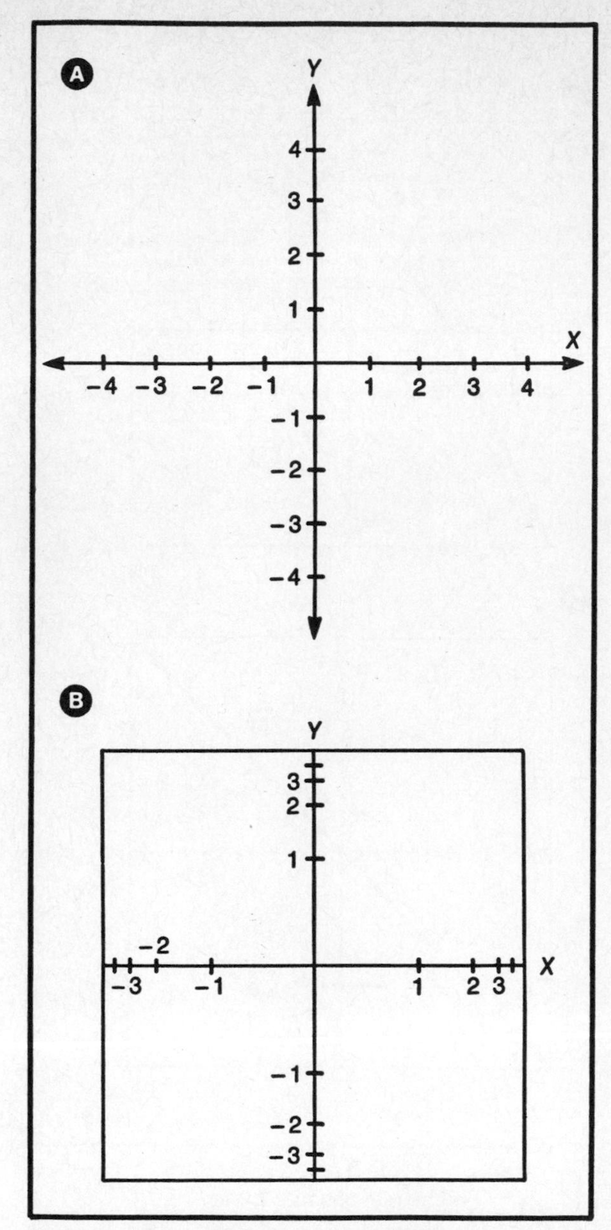

Fig. 1-5. A shows the Cartesian coordinate plane with linear axes. B shows a compressed coordinate plane using the principle of infinite series with a finite sum.

do this with the other three axes to get the graph plane at Fig. 1-5B.

Fractional values appear at intermediate points in this coordinate "plane segment." Actually, the point for ½ is a little closer to the point for 1, than to the point for 0; the point for 3⁄2 is a little closer to 2 than to 1, and so on. We won't bother to figure out the exact function to determine the precise locations of these points, except to note that we could if we wanted. The main purpose for pulling this little trick is to illustrate how we can, by means of this coordinate system, graph entire functions, even though they are grossly distorted near the outer boundaries of the plane.

Four different functions are shown in Fig. 1-6. The simple straight line $y = x$ is graphed at A. This line is straight even on this plane; however, lines with any slope besides 1 or −1, or are 0 or undefined (vertical) will not appear straight. A few examples are shown at B, where we see graphs of lines $y = 2x$, $y = -3x - 1$, and $y = 5x + 3$. On a linear-scale Cartesian plane these would be straight lines.

There is nothing especially wrong with a coordinate plane that does not show linear functions as straight lines. We do this all the time when we use semi-log or log-log graphing systems. The unique thing about this plane is the fact that it is only of finite size, and yet, if we are willing, we can denote any point on a function within this space. We are free to change the scale, say by a factor of 10, such as in Fig. 1-6C, or we can have unequal scales such as is the case at D.

You might want to play around with this coordinate system and graph some different functions on different scales. What seems to happen to the value of a function as the independent variable gets larger and larger without bound? This is easy to see by means of this graph. When x "approaches infinity," it does not necessarily follow that y will also. The value of y might approach any value. Consider, for example, $y = 1/(x + 1)$.

It is clear now what the frog would have to do in order to reach the wall. If he could jump faster and faster, doubling his jump frequency with each succeeding leap, he could reach the wall in a finite amount of time. He would look pretty silly doing this, and of course it is physically impossible, but in theory it can be done, and that is part of the beauty of mathematics. The physically impossible is not necessarily out of reach of the imagination.

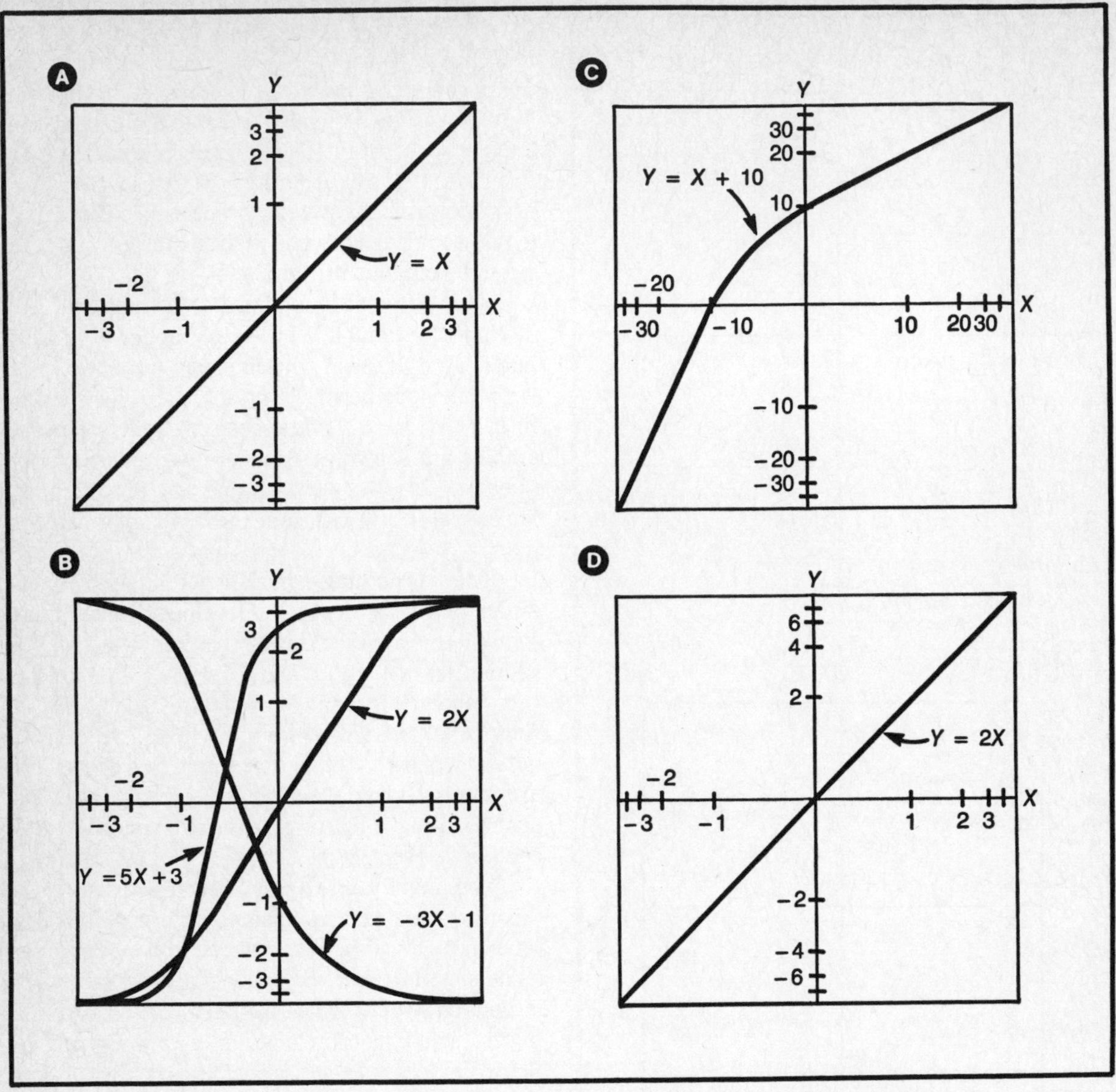

Fig. 1-6. Four examples of functions on "infinite coordinate planes." At A, $y = x$; at B, $y = 2x$, $y = -3x - 1$ and $y = 5x + 3$. At C and D, examples of functions $y = x + 10$ and $y = 2x$ on graphs with unequal scales.

PAINTING AN INFINITE SURFACE

Infinite quantities can be expressed in finite terms when we allow the imagination to run riot. Sometimes the relationship results in truly bizarre conclusions, such as the theoretical demonstration that we can paint an infinite surface area with a finite amount of paint—and still have plenty of paint left over.

Consider the function $f(x) = +(\pm 1/x)$. This function is graphed as shown in Fig. 1-7A. The function "blows up" at the point $x = 0$, and approaches 0 as the value of x gets arbitrarily large in either the positive or negative direction. The length of the function line is clearly infinite, as can be seen from a casual observation of the graph. In fact, the length is infinite even when we cut the

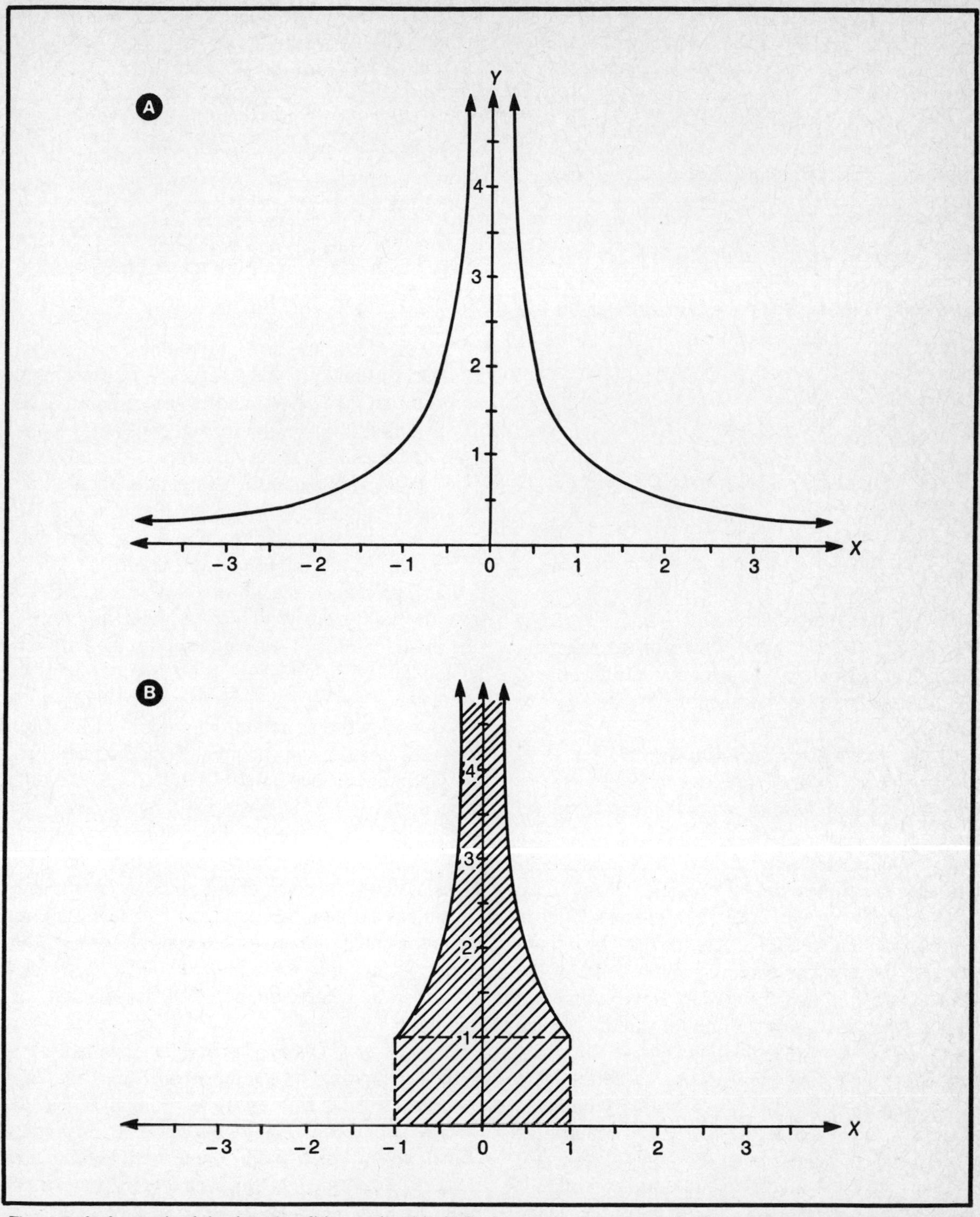

Fig. 1-7. At A, graph of the function $f(x) = +(\pm 1/x)$. At B, the graph of the same function between the limiting values $x = -1$ and $x = 1$, showing the interior area.

graph off, so that it is limited to the range $-1 \leq x < 1$ (Fig. 1-7B). The curve extends without limit in the positive ordinate direction. The value at $x = 0$ is undefined.

This function can, however, be integrated, and the area within the curve above the x axis can be determined. The indefinite integral of the positive part of the function, $f_+(x) = 1/x$, is

$$\int f_+(x)\,dx = \int (1/x)\,dx = e^x + c,$$

where c is a constant. If we integrate from 0 to 1, we get the area under the curve from $x = 0$ to $x = 1$:

$$\int_0^1 f_+(x)\,dx = e^1 - e^0 = e - 1 = 1.718$$

The function from $x = -1$ to $x = 0$ is an exact mirror image of the function from $x = 0$ to $x = 1$. Therefore

$$\int_{-1}^0 f_-(x)\,dx = \int_0^1 f_+(x)\,dx = e - 1 = 1.718$$

and the total area between $x = -1$ and $x = 1$ is therefore $2(e - 1) = 3.436$. This is an approximate value, because we have approximated the value of the irrational number e, assuming it to be equal to 2.718.

Now we have an interesting situation: a curve with an infinite outer perimeter but a finite interior area! It is not too hard to make the leap from two dimensions to three, simply by rotating this graph to get a funnel-shaped surface with an infinite surface area but a finite interior volume. Then, all we need to do is turn the object upside down, pour in the required amount of paint (which will be a finite amount, because the volume is finite) and let the funnel-shaped thing get filled up. Never mind that the paint would require an infinite amount of time to get all the way down the funnel; never mind that the funnel would get too narrow to accommodate the molecules of paint. In the imaginary universe of the mind, neither of these physical constraints are of concern. We can paint the whole surface just by filling up the funnel-shaped thing. And what is more, we can scoop out plenty of extra paint, and fill up a smaller, identically shaped object, and repeat this process, over and over—so that we can paint an infinite number of little funnel-shaped objects, each having infinite surface area, all with a finite amount of paint. The second object might be half the size of the first, the third half the size of the second, and so on, *ad infinitum.*

THE A.M./P.M. DILEMMA

We now change our perspective from space to time, which can provide as many problems and paradoxes as anything else in the mathematical cosmos.

Most of us are used to telling time in the 12-hour system. We speak of the a.m. (morning) and the p.m. (afternoon and evening) hours. The day begins at 12:00 midnight and ends at the same time 24 hours later. One minute past midnight is 12:01 a.m. and one minute before midnight is 11:59 p.m. the previous day. Similarly, around noontime, 12:01 p.m. represents one minute past noon and 11:59 a.m. is one minute before noon.

The problem comes in when we speak of 12:00 a.m. or 12:00 p.m. Which one is noon and which one is midnight? It isn't clear, all by itself, which should be which. This can cause, and has caused, confusion.

Consider the situation where it is 11:59 p.m. some day, that is, just one minute prior to midnight. We count off the seconds: 11:59:01, 11:59:02, and so on up till 11:59:59. We are still in the p.m., just one second before the witching hour. We can further divide this into tenths, hundredths, or even thousandths of seconds, or as fine as we care to get. As long as a given instant occurs before midnight, we are in the p.m. And any instant after midnight is part of the a.m.—even 12:00:00.0000001, for example. But what about the exact instant of midnight?

Since 12 follows 11, we might want to call midnight 12:00 p.m. The numbers have been building up from 11 to 12. But most often, midnight is considered 12:00 a.m. We'd better get it straight. Which will it be? Maybe you've seen legal documents stating that such-and-such is to commence effective 12:01 a.m. on a particular day. Now you know why they say 12:01 instead of 12:00. It's to

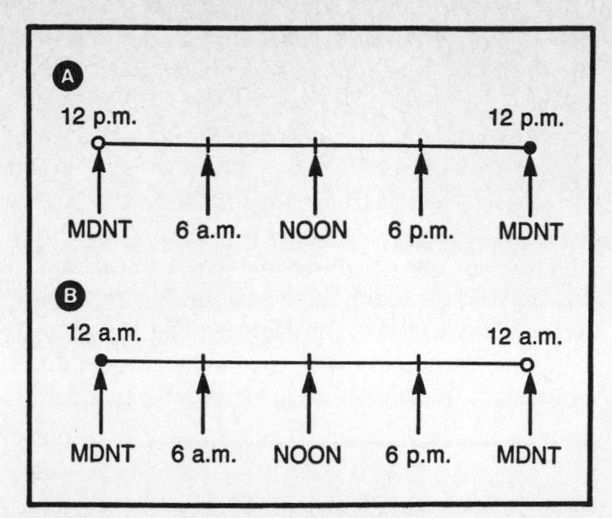

Fig. 1-8. The day is a half-open interval. If we consider midnight to be part of the p.m., as at A, the interval is closed at the end of the day. If we consider midnight to be part of the a.m., as at B, the interval is closed at the start of the day.

avoid confusion. Nobody really knows, or can prove one way or the other, whether midnight is 12:00 p.m. or 12:00 a.m. The convention is not well enough established for everybody to know it.

Actually, we can say either that midnight is part of the a.m. or part of the p.m. and the same goes for noon. It doesn't matter from a mathematical standpoint which one we choose. If we choose midnight as part of the p.m., then a day is a half-open interval, closed at the finish (Fig. 1-8A). If we choose midnight as part of the a.m., our day is a half-open interval, closed at the beginning (Fig. 1-8B). The military, using their 24-hour system, generally considers the day to begin at 0000 hours, making it a half-open interval closed at the beginning. There is no such thing as 2400 hours; this is thought of as 0000 the next day. But in civilian practice we mess things up by calling midnight and noon 12:00. We really ought to call them 0:00 (zero o'clock). But we'll never change. We've got to do things the hard way. Meanwhile, if you write a legal document to take place on a certain day, make sure you know which day you're talking about!

ONE POINT IN TIME

We might wonder whether there really exists such a thing as the instant of midnight or the instant of noon. A point in space is considered to have no height, no width, and no depth. On a line, a point has no length. In time, a point theoretically has no duration at all, and this might lead us to dismiss the foregoing a.m./p.m. dilemma as a bunch of nonsense—until it ends up in court for some reason that costs us a few thousand dollars to argue over.

Time is often thought of as the "past," "present," and "future," which can be illustrated on a "time line" as shown in Fig. 1-9. The past and future are half-lines, or rays without end points, and are infinitely long. The present is a point, in theory, that moves along the line. Events have a certain beginning, duration, and end. Several events are shown in Fig. 1-9 as line segments.

The present is unique in that it is a point having no dimensions. We might be led to wonder how we can even be aware of the present if it has no "size" on the time line. No matter how tiny an instant, no matter how short the duration of an event, the present lasts for an even shorter time—no time at all—and yet we are always there. It is an event of infinite duration yet consists of just a single point. "Tomorrow never comes; it's always today" is more than just a trivial phrase. It is true.

If the present has no duration, how can we be aware of it? Maybe in fact the present does have

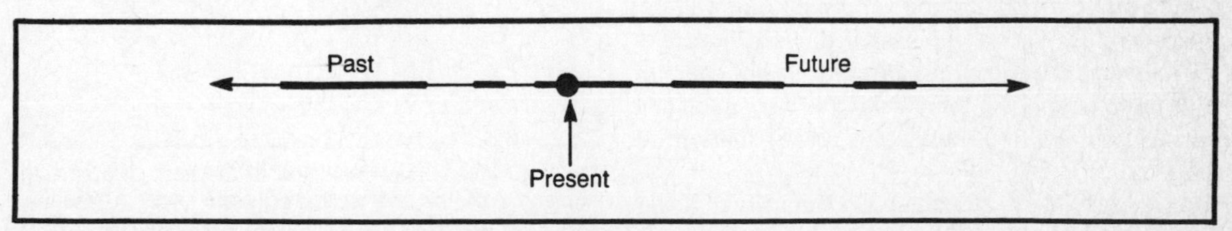

Fig. 1-9. The time line contains the past, present (a single point), and the future. Events are shown here as heavy line segments.

some dimensional value on the time line. It is possible that there is a smallest interval of time, a time particle, and we cannot have anything smaller. This appears to be true of matter, and it could be that it is also the case with time.

If there is indeed a shortest possible time interval, what is it? A billionth of a second? A trillionth? One good idea is that it is the time required by light to travel from one side of the smallest known particle to the other side. Whatever the shortest possible time is—if it is not zero—a degree of imperfection is introduced into the universe, a measure of uncertainty that we cannot resolve. This factor places a limit on the frequency of an energy wave; it determines how accurately we can pinpoint an event in time; it even places a fuzziness on time itself that cannot be clarified completely.

Whatever this smallest "time particle" might be, we know we haven't encountered it yet. A measuring apparatus has not yet been devised with enough precision so that this becomes a factor. So for now, we have to leave it to imagination, and continue to wonder about the paradox of the present being a point in time with no duration, but within which we are forever imprisoned as we move along toward our future.

IS THE FUTURE PREDESTINED?

This is an old philosophical question. Modern thought tends toward the idea that future events are left up to chance, or perhaps their occurrence is to some extent the result of certain causative factors, but that the future is not entirely predetermined. There really is no sound basis for this belief. We believe it because we want it to be that way. It bothers us to think that everything might be laid out, all ready to happen, and that all we need to do is wait and there is nothing we can do one way or the other. This is an unpleasant thought because it deprives us of our all-important sense of control over our destiny. But there are some very good arguments in favor of the idea of predestination in time.

Our universe is actually four-dimensional if we consider time to be a dimension. Albert Einstein was one of the first to point this out. He in fact made illustrations of time acting as a dimension. In order to do this, it is of course necessary to remove one physical dimension from the drawing and replace it with the time dimension. But this does not always present a problem.

Consider the circling airplane shown in Fig. 1-10A. At any given time the airplane is in a certain position, and after a certain length of time the airplane returns to the same position, having completed a circle. We might suppose that the plane takes one minute to make one circle. If we add a time axis to this illustration, and make the time axis

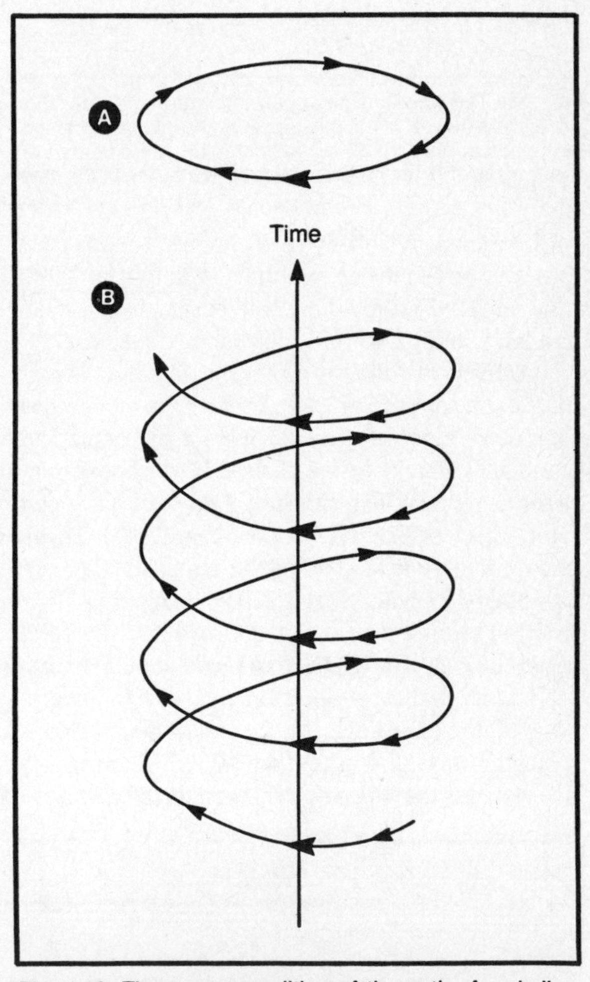

Fig. 1-10. Time-space rendition of the path of a circling airplane. At A, the path as we might see it from a distance, looking horizontally. At B, the path as shown with time added as the vertical axis (replacing altitude, which is assumed to be constant).

perpendicular to the plane in which the airplane is circling, and let the point of the present move along this axis from bottom to top, we obtain a helix as the path of the airplane through time-space (Fig. 1-10B). The time line can be marked off in intervals of one minute, and the pitch of the helix then becomes one division per revolution. This helix is a fixed object in time-space. As long as the airplane keeps on circling, we can predict exactly where it will be at any given time.

Oh, you say, but suppose the airplane crashes or changes its path or rate of circling. Then we cannot really predict its path, can we? This is the point of the philosophical argument: what will be will be, and what won't be, won't. Whatever the plane does, its path is a fixed curve in time-space. More subjectively, you might die tomorrow, and you might not; probably (and hopefully) not. But either you will or you won't. While we won't know till tomorrow evening, one thing is certain: what will be will be. It sounds almost too simple to make any sense, but the events that happen tomorrow are going to happen. Those that don't happen will not happen. Things will take place in one specific way, and only one way. While we can't be certain, at least by presently known scientific means, what will take place, we can be sure that something will, and it will happen in a certain way. The four-dimensional structure of events in time-space is a fixed thing. It can't be changed, because it, in the reality of four-space, already *is*.

HOW MANY NUMBERS ARE THERE?

When you were a little child you probably went through a counting experience, where you spent the better part of a morning or afternoon getting up to 1,000 or even 2,000. You were making the discovery that you could always find another number larger than any given number. The positive integers, or "counting numbers," are infinite in number. The set of positive integers is customarily written

$$N = \{1,2,3,4,5, \ldots\}$$

where N stands for their formal name, the natural numbers. There is something interesting about these numbers: we can list them. We can arrange them in a manner such that, given part of the list, we can say what the next number on the list will be. We can *denumerate* the positive integers.

It is just a short step to add zero and the negative integers. We might say that the set of integers, S, is the union of the following three sets, the elements of which are denumerable:

$$N_+ = \{1,2,3,4,5, \ldots\}$$
$$\{0\} = \{0\}$$
$$N_- = \{-1,-2,-3,-4,-5, \ldots\}$$

and it follows that $S = N_+ \; U \{0\} \; U N_-$.

The *rational numbers* are those numbers of the form a/b, where a is any integer and b is a positive integer. If we consider the positive rational numbers, a and b are both positive integers. No matter what rational number we may choose, we can write it in this fractional form. It may take a lot of work to find that form, but it can be found. Similarly, any number of the form a/b, where a and b are positive integers, is a positive rational number. These two facts result in a one-to-one correspondence, or *homomorphism*, between the set of positive rationals and the set of numbers a/b where a and b are positive integers.

We can in fact make a list of all the rational numbers. In order to make a list that is denumerable, we must do more than simply write down numbers. There has to be some way to list them so that we know we will reach any given number if we continue long enough down the list. Figure 1-11 shows an array of the positive rational numbers, listed in an orderly way, and illustrates a method of proceeding down the list so that every number will sooner or later be hit. We can identify all of these numbers one by one, and therefore assign a positive integer to each of them. In the case of Fig. 1-11, the assignment is as follows:

$$1 \longleftrightarrow 1/1$$
$$2 \longleftrightarrow 2/1$$
$$3 \longleftrightarrow 1/2$$
$$4 \longleftrightarrow 3/1$$

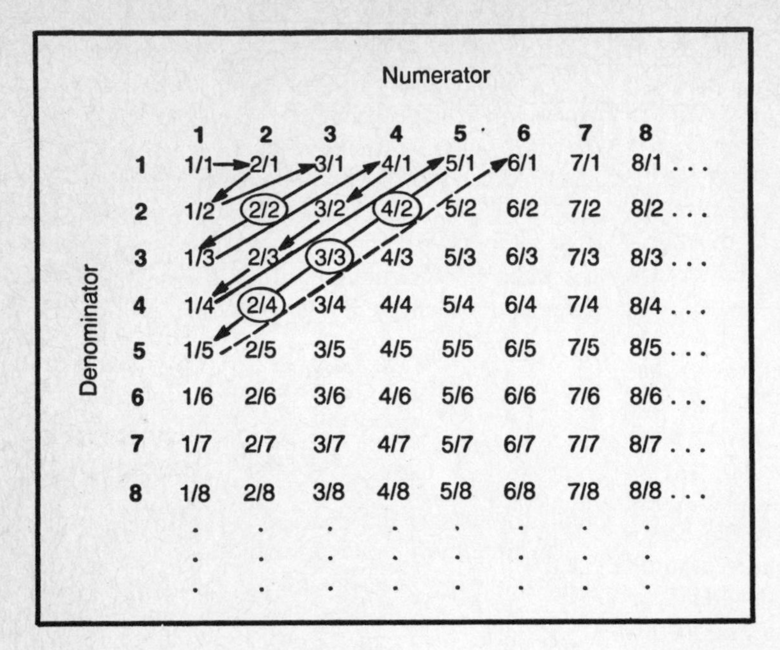

Fig. 1-11. An array of rational numbers, including all the positive rationals. Some values are repeated. In the counting scheme, they are skipped over. The positive rationals are in one-to-one correspondence with the positive integers.

$$
\begin{aligned}
5 &\longleftrightarrow \tfrac{1}{3}\\
6 &\longleftrightarrow \tfrac{4}{1}\\
7 &\longleftrightarrow \tfrac{3}{2}\\
8 &\longleftrightarrow \tfrac{2}{3}\\
9 &\longleftrightarrow \tfrac{1}{4}\\
10 &\longleftrightarrow \tfrac{5}{1}\\
11 &\longleftrightarrow \tfrac{1}{5}
\end{aligned}
$$

Note that we skip over numbers that have been previously identified. For example, $\frac{4}{2} = 2$, $\frac{3}{3} = 1$ and $\frac{2}{4} = \frac{1}{2}$, all of which have been touched already. This eliminates ambiguities.

The number of elements in a set is called its *cardinal number*. The cardinal number of the empty set, for example, is 0; the cardinal number of the set of natural numbers up to, and including, 100, is 100. The cardinal number of all natural numbers is infinite, and has been given the name *aleph nought*, written $\aleph_0$. We say that two sets have the same cardinal number if and only if there exists a one-to-one correspondence between the elements of the sets. The set of natural numbers, N, has the same cardinality as the set of positive rational numbers, which we might call R_+. In fact the cardinality of the set of all rationals is aleph nought.

This seems peculiar—to say that there are no more rational numbers than natural numbers. However, it has been proven. The set of even natural numbers is the same size as the set of all natural numbers; in fact the set of natural numbers divisible by 10,000 is the same size as the set of all natural numbers, and hence as the set of all rational numbers. With the real numbers, however, we encounter a problem.

Let's consider the set of all real numbers between 0 and 1, and including both 0 and 1. Such numbers have decimal expansions of the form $0.a_1a_2a_3 \ldots$ where a_i for natural numbers $_i$ are digits 0, 1, 2, 3, 4, 5, 6, 7, 8, or 9. At least we believe this to be so. Some of the decimals are repeating, and some reach a certain point and then continue on with a string of zeros. For example,

$$
\begin{aligned}
\tfrac{1}{2} &= 0.50000000000\ldots\\
\tfrac{2}{3} &= 0.66666666666\ldots\\
\tfrac{1}{8} &= 0.12500000000\ldots\\
\tfrac{37}{999} &= 0.03703703703\ldots\\
\pi - 3 &= 0.14159265358\ldots
\end{aligned}
$$

This last example is a nonterminating, nonrepeating decimal, an irrational number.

Suppose we set out to make a list of all real numbers between 0 and 1. We might make an array such as is shown in Fig. 1-12. We number the

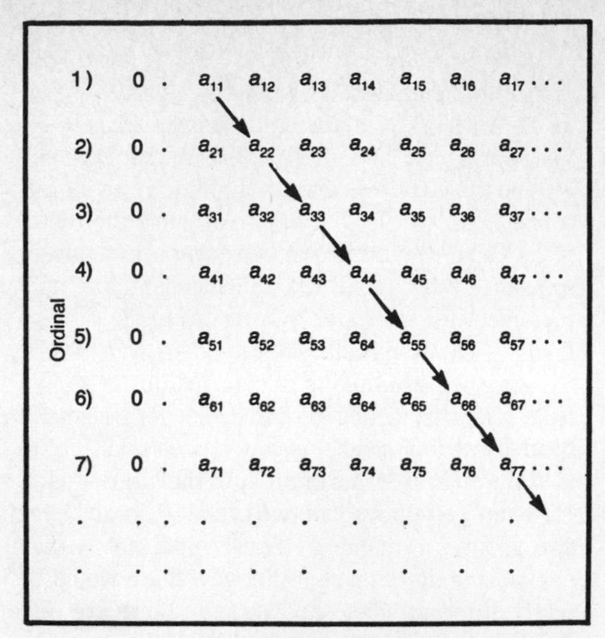

Fig. 1-12. An attempt at listing all of the real numbers between, and including, 0 and 1. It is simple to construct a number that is different from all of them, as shown by the arrows and discussed in the text.

a_{ij} by denoting the row number i and the column number j, where rows are horizontal and columns are vertical. We can choose any number from the set $\{0,1,2,3,4,5,6,7,8,9\}$ as a given a_{ij}. It is clear that we will get an infinitely long list of infinitely long decimal expansions. Can we, if we were able to keep listing for all natural numbers i and j, ever list all of the real numbers between 0 and 1? The answer is no, and this is easy to prove.

Consider the number $0.a_{11}a_{22}a_{33}\ldots$, constructed by proceeding down this hopefully complete list of real numbers between 0 and 1. This number may eventually appear on the list. But now consider the number $0.b_{11}b_{22}b_{33}\ldots$, such that for all b_{ii}, $b_{ii} \neq a_{ii}$. That is, we choose any of the nine digits different from a_{ii} in a given case. Such a number cannot possibly be in this list. One digit, and at least one, is different no matter how far down the list we go. There are real numbers, therefore, that do not appear on the list of decimal expansions. We cannot get a one-to-one correspondence between the natural numbers and the real numbers between 0 and 1 in this way.

It is possible that there exists some other way to list the reals between 0 and 1, but it has not yet been found. We call the set of reals between 0 and 1 *nondenumerable*. It has a cardinality greater than $\aleph_0$. We say that the real numbers between 0 and 1 have cardinality aleph one, or $\aleph_1$, and that $\aleph_1 > \aleph_0$.

This is a peculiar thing indeed. The cardinal number $\aleph_0$ is infinite in the sense that it is larger than any natural number. Yet, there exists an "infinity" even bigger than this! Might there exist "infinities" still larger? Mathematicians think so. There might even be a countably infinite hierarchy of "infinities," known formally as *transfinite cardinal numbers*.

There are other ways to look at "infinity" besides this, and we will examine one of these perspectives later. Now, let's change to a lighter frame of mind, and play some games. You might want to take a set of toothpicks or matches along with you to your next social encounter where trivia are likely to be discussed.

TOOTHPICK GAMES

Rearranging sticks to form new patterns, using the least possible (or an exact) number of moves is an old mathematical game that has endless variations. Sometimes a "trick" is involved that we

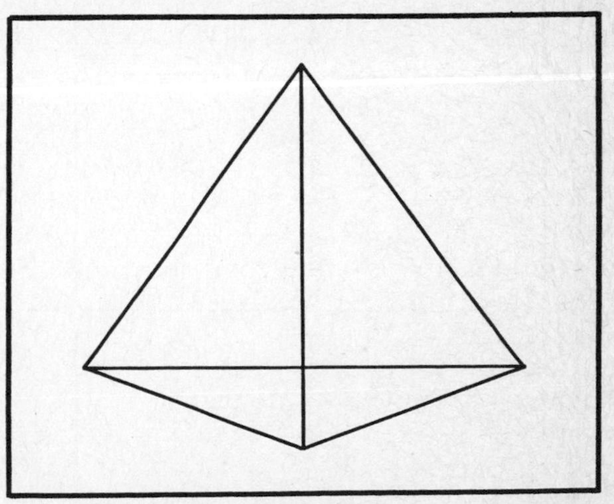

Fig. 1-13. Arranging six equal sticks so that four equilateral triangles are obtained. The process is three-dimensional, and the result is a regular tetrahedron.

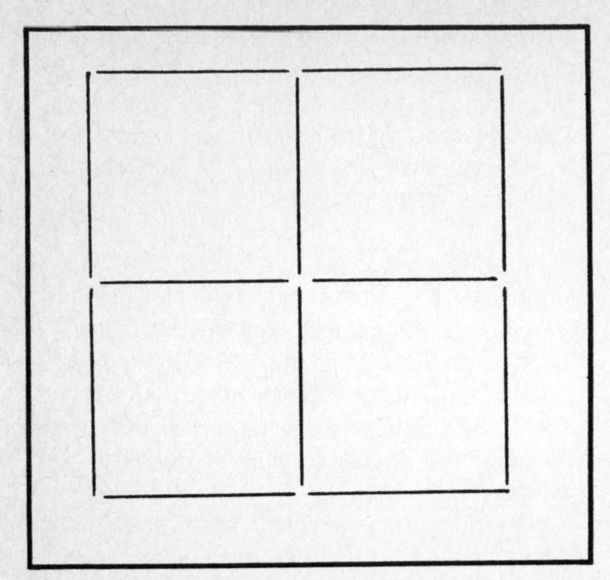

Fig. 1-14. Remove two sticks, leaving two squares without having any sticks not part of a square.

wouldn't ordinarily think of; this makes such games a little like mathematical proofs where the solution is obvious—if we have the right way of looking at it.

A good example is the positioning of six equal-sized toothpicks to form a figure with four equilateral triangles. The toothpicks are to make up the sides of the equilateral triangles. Placing the toothpicks on a table, it would seem that this task is impossible. But we are not limited to two dimensions. If we can find a way to support the toothpicks above the table, we can form a pyramid or regular tetrahedron (three-dimensional figure with four identical sides), as shown in Fig. 1-13. This gives us the required solution.

Another example is shown in Fig. 1-14. We have 12 sticks, arranged so that they form a square divided into four smaller squares. Each small square is ¼ the size, in terms of area, of the large square. How can we remove just two of the sticks and have two squares remaining? There must not be any sticks hanging out free; otherwise there would be many different solutions. Actually there are four different ways to remove exactly two sticks, leaving two complete squares without any sticks hanging free. The solution—one of the four—is shown in Appendix A.

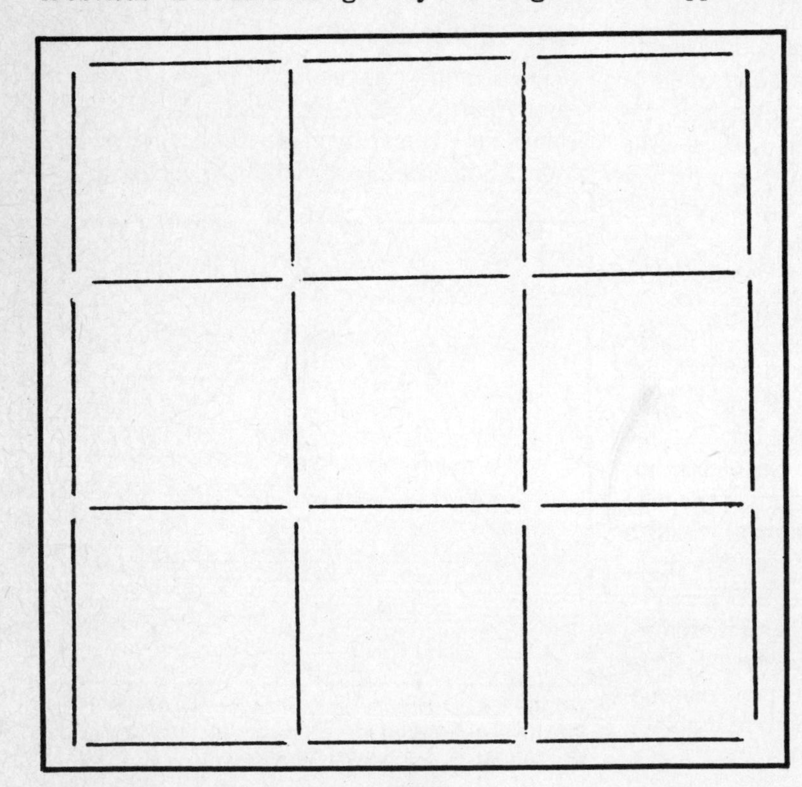

Fig. 1-15. Remove four sticks to obtain five squares, without having any sticks not part of a square.

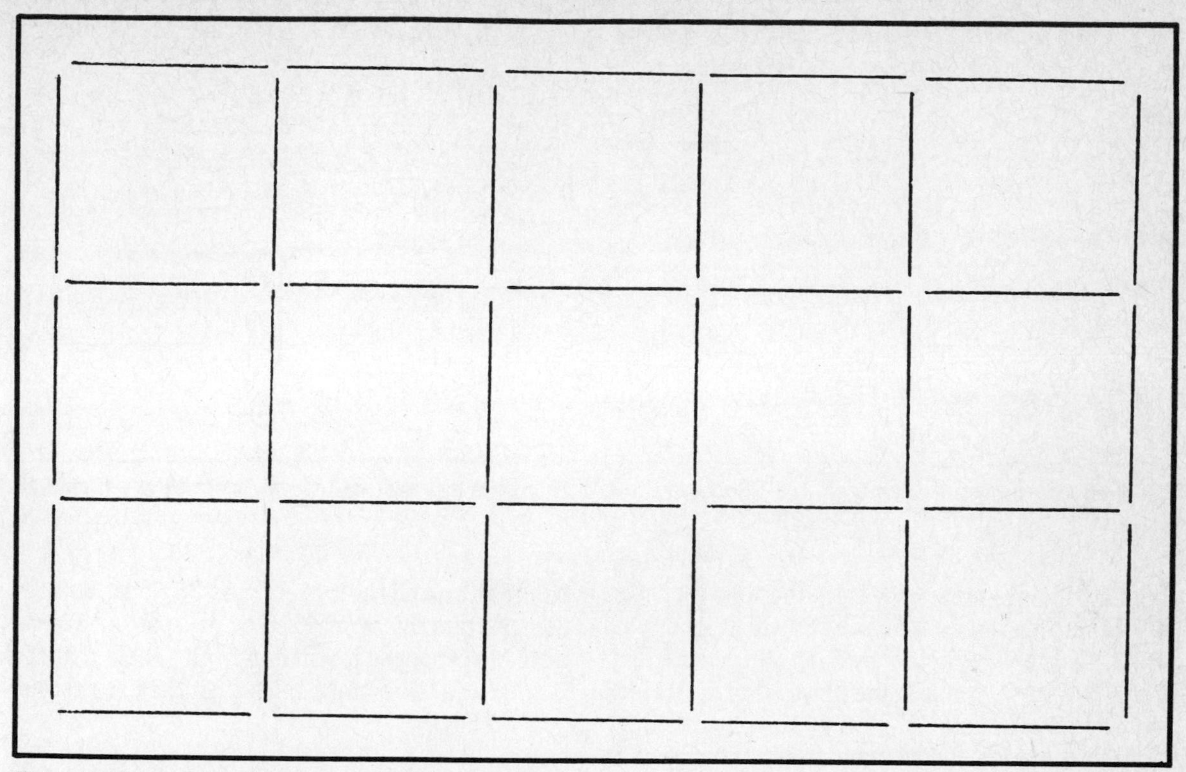

Fig. 1-16. Remove 14 sticks, leaving six identical squares. Every stick remaining must form part of a square.

A similar, but more complicated, problem is shown in Fig. 1-15. We must remove four sticks from this pattern to obtain five squares. Again, there cannot be any sticks left over. The solution is in Appendix A.

A still more sophisticated problem of this same type involves the pattern shown in Fig. 1-16, where there are 36 sticks arranged to make 15 small squares. We must remove 14 of these sticks, leaving six identical squares. A solution is given in Appendix A.

A somewhat different problem is shown in Fig. 1-17. Here, we have a spiral-like pattern formed by 15 sticks. We can move just three of these, obtaining two squares. How? Try it for a while and then, if you can't get the solution, refer to Appendix A.

An interesting trick, a sort of optical illusion, can be played using sticks or, if you prefer, just a paper and pencil. Certain irregular polygons actually have many more sides than they at first seem to have. Take a very brief glance at A, B and C in

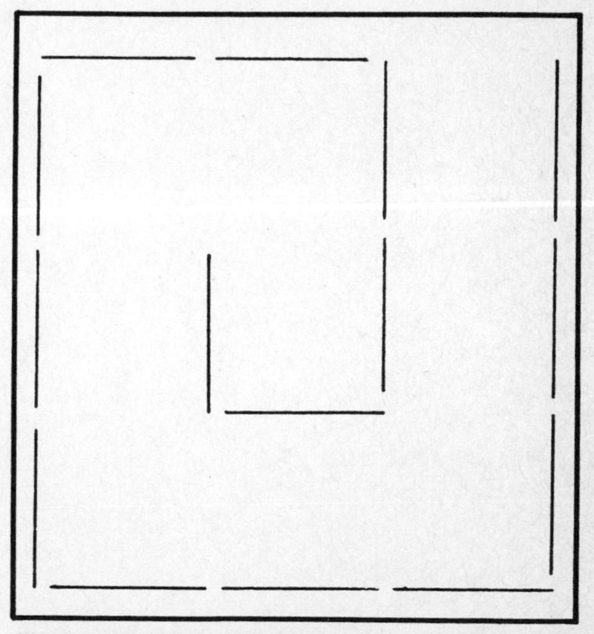

Fig. 1-17. Move three of these sticks to get two squares. All sticks must form part of a square.

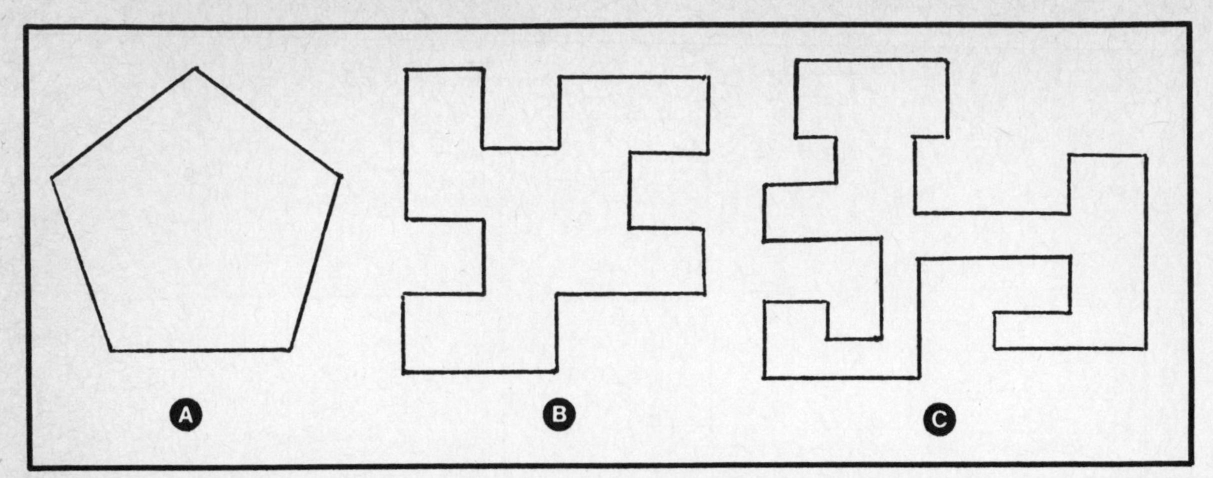

Fig. 1-18. At A, a regular pentagon (five sides), At B and C, polygons that have deceptively more sides—18 and 26, respectively—than they at first appear to have.

Fig. 1-18. How many sides are there in each figure? The drawing at A is a regular pentagon; you can probably tell within a fraction of a second that it has five sides. Blink at the illustration in B. How many sides are there? Blink at C. How many sides? It might surprise you to know that the figure at B has 18 sides and the one at C has 26 sides. You can demonstrate this at parties and get quite a wide variety of responses if you don't tell people that the figures will have more sides than they at first appear to have.

Chapter 2

The Vagaries of Logic

LOGIC IS THE FOUNDATION BY WHICH WE, AND IN fact all beings, carry out our thought processes. A discussion of the elements of logic might at first seem superfluous, or even worse, tautological; how can we talk about how we talk about things? In a way, this is a little like trying to pull oneself up by one's own bootstraps. But some mathematicians devote their entire careers to just this subject. And logic is indispensable in the art of law practice, and in fact in every endeavor.

A MEDICAL EXAMPLE

I don't claim to have any special medical knowledge, but I will give an example of a possible logical flaw in medical reasoning that could lead to a wrong conclusion—or maybe the right one, but by accident.

There has recently been a great deal of evidence gathered linking high levels of cholesterol in the blood to heart disease. When people have high cholesterol levels, they have a greater tendency to have or develop heart disease. Conversely, those with heart disease generally have more of this substance in their blood than people without heart disease. This is a proven fact, verified by experiment.

The first conclusion reached by medical people was this: we ought to try to lower the level of cholesterol in our blood streams, so that we will be less likely to develop heart disease. The easiest way (or at least the simplest) is by means of diet. It is generally thought that a low-fat, low-cholesterol diet causes the level of serum cholesterol to go down. I myself have found this to be true for my body. It might not work for some people, but it does for me. So far, everything is in order, because we have dealt only with experimental data.

But will a low-fat, low-cholesterol diet really reduce my chances of getting heart disease? My doctors say it will. On what logic do they base this?

Suppose for a moment that heart disease is caused by something we haven't ever even thought might have anything to do with our health, such as rapid acceleration and deceleration we experience every day when we drive in cars or fly in airplanes. It sounds silly, but let's keep going. Imagine that heart disease is caused by some by-product of modern civilization, such as reduced physical activity, or by some additive that we put in food nowadays to keep it fresh or to make it look better or taste better. If you want to go to the extreme, suppose it is caused by radiation, such as X-rays that we get in clinics and hospitals, or even from watching television! Suppose that electromagnetic fields from broadcast stations and electrical wires create some disturbance in our cells that causes heart disease! Suppose that the high cholesterol level found in heart patients is a symptom, not a cause, of their problem. Then, a low-fat, low-cholesterol diet might not help me.

I'm not a doctor and certainly recommend that people listen to their doctors, not me, when it comes to diet and exercise and health in general. But to say that a high-fat, high-cholesterol diet will cause heart disease is an assumption not based on pure mathematical logic. If two events or situations, call them A and B, are found to be correlated, we have no way of knowing which one is the cause and which is the effect, or whether they might both be the result of some other unknown, C. We can illustrate this in the form of a diagram, such as Fig. 2-1. In this illustration, A represents high blood cholesterol, B represents heart disease, and C represents an unknown that causes both A and B. Perhaps C is a bad diet, too high in fat and cholesterol; maybe C is lack of exercise, or too much salt, or not enough fiber, or radiation, or electromagnetic energy, or acceleration, or some combination of these—or something we've never thought of at all. The lesson: don't jump to conclusions that aren't warranted.

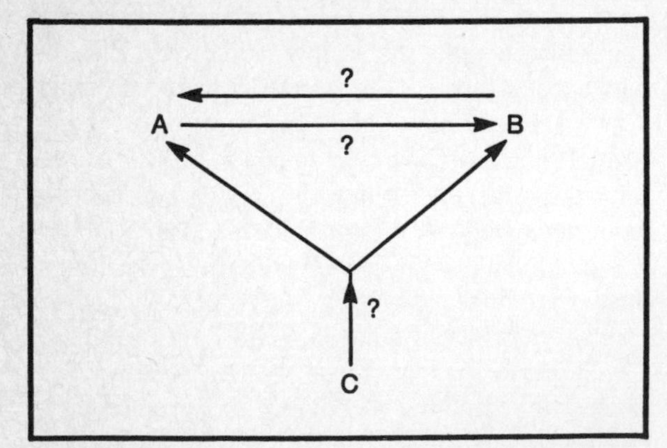

Fig. 2-1. If two events, A and B, are found to be correlated, we do not know whether A causes B or whether B causes A, or whether they might both be the result of some other cause, C.

Table 2-1. Truth Table for Negation, Conjunction, and Disjunction Operations.

X	Y	$-X$	XY	$X+Y$
0	0	1	0	0
0	1	1	0	1
1	0	0	0	1
1	1	0	1	1

THE LOGICAL OPERATIONS

In logic, there are three basic operations: negation, conjunction and disjunction. These are sometimes referred to as the NOT, AND, and OR operations. The symbology varies, but let's use the Boolean symbols here, where negation (the NOT operation) is symbolized by a minus sign (−), conjunction (the AND operation) by multiplication (no sign), and disjunction (the OR operation) by a plus sign (+). Statements are represented as capital letters. A statement represents a complete sentence in the simplest form of logic, known as *sentential logic.*

We denote these logical operations by means of tables, as shown in Table 2-1. Statements are indicated by letters X and Y. We see that if X and Y are both true, for example, then XY is true and $X+Y$ is also true. But $-X$ is false. Truth value is assigned either 0 (false) or 1 (true). A statement must be either true or false, but it cannot be both.

We should note that the OR operation is generally, unless otherwise specified, considered to be inclusive. This means that $X+Y$ is false only when both X and Y are false. The exclusive OR operation, sometimes used instead of the inclusive OR, is true if the truth values of X and Y differ, and false if the truth values are the same. This is shown in Table 2-2.

Truth tables can be used to determine whether or not two logical statements are equivalent. Two statements are equivalent if and only if they have

Table 2-2. Exclusive OR Operation Truth Table.

X	Y	$X+Y$ (exclusive OR)
0	0	0
0	1	1
1	0	1
1	1	0

identical truth values in every case. A simple example is X and $-(-X)$, double negation. More complicated examples are unlimited in their range of complexity. The equal sign (=) is used to signify logical equivalence.

Some common examples of logical equivalence are shown in Table 2-3. These are useful for proving more complex logical theorems. Sentential logic is similar to algebra in some ways, as can be seen from this table, and in fact the mathematician George Boole is often given credit for the development of a mathematical system of logic called Boolean algebra. It is used extensively in the design of digital electronic equipment, including computers and switching systems.

LOGICAL FUNCTIONS

Logical equivalence is one of the two major logical functions. The other is the "if-then" or implication function, symbolized by an arrow pointing toward the right. We write "X implies Y" or "If X, then Y" as $X \rightarrow Y$. Actually the word "implies" is a poor choice, because it gives the impression that perhaps Y might not be true if X is true. The implication function is strong since it means that Y is always true if X is true.

Implication does not work in reverse. That is, if $X \rightarrow Y$, it is not necessarily the case that $Y \rightarrow X$. These two statements are not logically equivalent. This fallacy is sometimes made in logical arguments, and can be used to produce results that aren't valid. Even scientists sometimes make this error. We might make statement X say "You have a coronary heart disease" and Y say "You have high blood cholesterol." The statement $X \rightarrow Y$ is almost true since most heart patients do have high cholesterol. But this says nothing about the reverse situation $Y \rightarrow X$. The association may be true in real life, but it is not implied *logically*.

Another example might be to say that if it is raining, there are clouds in the sky. This does not imply that if there are clouds in the sky, then it must be raining.

It is also true that $X \rightarrow Y = -Y \rightarrow -X$. Thus we can say that if there are no clouds in the sky, then it cannot be raining. We can say with reasonable accuracy also that if your blood cholesterol is low, you do not have coronary heart disease. The medical examples here are inexact, however, and the exceptions in case $X \rightarrow Y$ may be much different in magnitude from those in case $-Y \rightarrow -X$. When we attempt to apply the precision of mathematical logic to the inexact physical world, we are likely to get ourselves in trouble. This is part of the problem doctors are facing in the controversy over exactly how heart disease can be prevented. And I'm sure someone will come along, sooner or later, and say that it has rained from a cloudless sky!

DERIVATIONS

The rules of Boolean algebra shown in Table 2-3 can be employed to give proofs for various logical arguments. The proofs are carried out step by step, in tabular form, with "statements" in one column and "reasons" in the other. An example of

Table 2-3. Some Common Theorems of Boolean Algebra.

1. $X+0 = X$
2. $X1 = X$
3. $X+1 = 1$
4. $X0 = 0$
5. $X+X = X$
6. $XX = X$
7. $-(-X) = X$
8. $X+(-X) = 1$
9. $(-X)X = 0$
10. $X+Y = Y+X$
11. $XY = YX$
12. $X+XY = X$
13. $X(-Y)+Y = X+Y$
14. $X+Y+Z = (X+Y)+Z = X+(Y+Z)$
15. $XYZ = (XY)Z = X(YZ)$
16. $X(Y+Z) = XY + XZ$
17. $(X+W)(Y+Z) = XY+XZ+WY+WZ$

Table 2-4. A Proof That $-(X+(-X)) + (Y+1) = 1$, Using the Method of Statements and Reasons.

	Statements	Reasons
1.	$X+(-X) = 1$	Theorem 8
2.	$Y+1 = 1$	Theorem 3
3.	$(-X)X = 0$	Theorem 9
4.	$-[X+(-X)] = 0$	Statements 1, 3
5.	$1+0 = 1$	Known fact of +
6.	$-(X+(-X)) + (Y+1) = 1$	Statements 2, 4, 5

such a proof is shown in Table 2-4. Another method of proof, which demonstrates logical equivalence, is the truth-table method. An example of this is shown in Table 2-5.

Proofs in sentential logic become pretty boring after a while. Some proofs are fairly easy, but others very difficult and lengthy. Once a theorem has been proved, however, it can be employed in the proofs of other theorems. Eventually, very complicated proofs can be carried out in a short number of steps using an enormous repertoire of theorems that have been built up. The structure grows upon itself, like a tree. But should a contradiction ever be found, all of logic would collapse: a mathematical theory is no good if there is one single flaw in it. So far, no contradictions have been found in mathematical logic. We should hope none ever will be. But logic can be misused, with fallacious reasoning leading to apparent contradictions or ridiculous statements.

There are many kinds of subtle ways to misuse logic in everyday language. Sometimes ludicrous statements can be derived from apparently reasonable ones. We might say that some cats have striped tails, for example, and that my cat has a striped tail.

Table 2-5. Proof That $X(-Y)+Y = X+Y$ for All Possible Combinations of Truth Values of X and Y. This Is Done by Showing That the Truth Values of Both Statements Are Always Identical.

X	Y	$-Y$	$X(-Y)$	$X(-Y)+Y$	$X+Y$
0	0	1	0	0	0
0	1	0	0	1	1
1	0	1	1	1	1
1	1	0	0	1	1

Therefore, my cat is some cat! Let's look at some of the common ways that logic can be twisted in the language to "prove" things that aren't necessarily true.

BEGGING THE QUESTION

Sometimes we "prove" a statement by assuming that it is true to start out with. This can be done in subtle ways, so that we might even fool ourselves in the process. Those of you who are lawyers will recognize this fallacy often in the courtroom, and may have used it—knowingly or not—in your own arguments.

Begging the question doesn't prove anything logically, although the premise and the conclusion may both be quite true (they would have to be either both true or both false, of course, because they are logically equivalent). The logical statement $X \rightarrow X$ is the "proof" that takes place when we beg the question.

Here is an example of begging the question. Let us say that the temperature is −35 Fahrenheit and the wind speed is sustained at 40 miles per hour with gusts to 75 miles per hour. Then it is cold and windy outside. That is the conclusion, and it's doubtful that anyone would care to refute it. Though the conclusion is more general than the premise, we might say that the two are equivalent in a certain sense, although not logically identical.

We can get more subtle when we beg the question. "Allowing people to drive at unlimited speeds on the streets presents a threat to the community, because it is dangerous to the people to have cars moving at high speeds in residential areas." Actually the premise here is stated second and the conclusion first, but both the premise and the conclusion are saying the same thing. Nothing is established. We might as well just say one thing or the other; it is pointless to say both. Begging the question can be done in arguments having several "logical" steps, returning to the premise when the conclusion is finally reached.

MISTAKING THE CAUSE

Sometimes we draw conclusions that are unwarranted even though they appear to be related.

We might think that something implies or causes another event, when in reality the cause is quite different. Or we might think that one event causes another simply because they repeatedly occur together, or one repeatedly follows the other.

An example of mistaken cause is the clearing that follows a storm front. Thunderstorms are usually followed by clearer, cooler weather. But the storms do not cause the clearing and cooling; the real cause is much more complex. Nor does the cool, clear air, in and of itself, cause the storms. Again, there are several factors present.

The example discussed previously, involving the relationship between blood cholesterol and heart disease, is a possible example of this fallacy. But this is an enormously complicated matter where many different kinds of errors are possible in logical reasoning.

Another example of this fallacy is that drinking a glass of brandy every night before going to bed will cure a common cold, since every time you've done this, your cold has gone away in only a few days. Actually the brandy would probably prolong the cold, if anything. Yet how many times have you heard that you can "sweat out" a cold or flu by going to bed with a big bottle of booze?

GENERALIZATION

Often, an erroneous or unwarranted conclusion is drawn on the basis of too little data. This is the fallacy of the hasty generalization, assigning particular characteristiccs to something as a whole, based on an examination of too little data or the wrong data.

It might be that every time you ask out a member of the opposite sex after having just polished your shoes, she or he says "No." Certainly that does not imply that polishing shoes makes one less attractive to members of the opposite sex. This fallacy can be committed in more subtle ways. If taking paregoric relieves a stomach ache for someone several times, we might be led to think that paregoric should be administered every time anybody gets a stomach ache. Most doctors would beg to differ with that conclusion! Generalization is often used to prove a point that is emotionally appealing, or to get away without taking blame. "Oh, he always does that," we might say to excuse someone's behavior, even though it has happened only a few times.

IRRELEVANCE

Many arguments contain irrelevant statements that do not necessarily damage the logical validity of the argument, but can cause false conclusions to be drawn that have nothing to do with the intended argument. Such conclusions fail to prove the point at hand, although they may prove other possibly useful things. An irrelevant conclusion or conclusions can be used to appeal emotionally to an audience, "setting them up" so that they will accept the desired argument even though it has not even been addressed. An example of this is as follows: suppose legislation is being considered to reduce the speed limit on a particular stretch of highway. Someone may speak in favor of this proposal, stating that it is desirable to have reasonable speed limits on all roadways. This is a conclusion that has nothing to do with the particular road in question. It does nothing to establish the conclusion that the speed limit should be reduced there. Other conclusions might be things such as "We want to keep our roads safe for children" or "The speed limits are generally too high anyhow."

IMPROPER USE OF CONTEXT

The same word may have different meanings, and in a logical argument, we cannot change the intended meaning of a word in the course of the discussion. This can result in truly ridiculous statements. "A pen that has run out of ink is no good for keeping cows" is an example, where "pen" refers to a writing instrument first and an enclosure for animals second. The conclusion is certainly reasonable, although silly, but this is an extreme example.

A more subtle example of this is found in a dissertation that I read in a college philosophy course. The argument had to do with responsibility, and the word "responsible" was the victim of improper use of context. A person might be considered responsible for his actions. If he behaves in an irresponsible manner, such as stealing or mugging, this does not necessarily imply that he is not responsible for his actions. Yet this was the argument offered: whenever someone acts irresponsibly, he or she is not responsible for his or her actions, so it's not his or her fault. In that case I could shoot someone and then claim that I had nothing whatsoever to do with it, and be let off scot-free! Obviously irresponsible behavior is entirely different from not being responsible for one's actions.

APPEALS TO FORCE, AUTHORITY, POPULARITY AND PITY

Although not logical fallacies in the literal sense, we often use some crutch to convince our audience that what we say is true or valid. That crutch might be force, in which case we intend to scare our audience into accepting what we have to say; it might be authority, such as "I have a degree in such-and-such, and therefore I am right and you are wrong because you have no degree in that field." We can appeal to popularity, going along with the majority in order to get what we want; we can appeal to pity, saying something like "Help the poor children, raise taxes."

I can recall being argued against in all four of these ways. One incident is especially interesting. I was involved in a discussion on whether or not reducing the bandwidth of a signal would increase the signal-to-noise ratio. The other fellow appealed to his advanced degree, which he supposedly had, and concluded that his notion—reducing the bandwidth would make no difference—was right, purely on the basis of his advanced degree.

An example of this, and also of appeal to popularity, can be found in the refutation of Immanuel Velikovsky's theory that Venus was a comet at one time, ejected from the planet Jupiter and passing near the earth twice. Velikovsky claimed that this occurred several thousand years ago, causing catastrophes that are documented in various religions. Scientists were quick to point out that Velikovsky was not an astronomer, having no degree, and that, aside from being grossly improbable, his theories were based on inferior intellect. Most scientists disagreed with Velikovsky; therefore Velikovsky had to be wrong. Whether his theory has any validity or not, the arguments against it were not always based on logic, but often on emotion and pride.

Appeals to force, authority, popularity and pity are often used in combination with each other. In the Velikovsky case, appeals to authority and popularity were used in combination. Most scientists are somewhat emotionally attached to their theories, and will often defend them without logical basis. The most dangerous is the appeal to force, where one professor might attack his colleague by attempting to have him removed from his post. Believe it or not, things like this happen, although fortunately they are rare.

CIRCUMSTANTIAL EVIDENCE

Arguments are often made by proving certain facts that lead a listener to believe that a certain conclusion can be reasonably reached. This is not a strictly logical means of argument, since the conclusion is inferred but not absolutely proven.

An example of circumstantial evidence might be found in a courtroom trial, when a lawyer "sets up" several witnesses by asking questions not directly related to the issue at hand. Several witnesses might say that they saw the accused in the vicinity of the place where a crime occurred, but this does not logically imply that the accused committed the crime.

APPEAL TO CIRCUMSTANCE

We can try to get someone to believe what we say on account of that person's special circumstances. We might tell a doctor that we shouldn't take a certain medicine because it isn't good medical practice to take a drug if we don't absolutely require it. The doctor may know reasons we should take the medicine that we aren't aware of, but an appeal to his professional expertise might sway him. A man of logic would not be fooled.

The appeal to circumstance is an example of arguing to the person instead of to the premise and conclusion at hand. It is another form of emotional appeal, similar to the appeal to authority, except that the authority is in this case the opponent in the argument, and we are trying to "butter him up."

Sometimes the appeal to circumstance takes the form of an affront. For example, we might say, "What kind of doctor are you, prescribing a medicine that does no good?" This is related to the appeal to force; such a statement, in view of the conditions nowadays, contains an implied threat of a malpractice suit. We might also attack a third party, arguing that so-and-so was fired because he was dishonest or had a bad personality, when the real reason might be that he wasn't doing his job.

FAULTY SYLLOGISMS

The preceding examples of non-logical arguments are not true fallacies. They are quite common schemes for making something illogical appear to be logical. Outright logical errors are sometimes made, however, that are not obviously apparent and can lead to ridiculous conclusions.

A syllogism is an argument where a conclusion is drawn based on two premises. The first premise might be a disjunction or an "if-then" statement. An example of a disjunctive syllogism is the following: "Either you are in Florida or you are in New York; you aren't in Florida, so therefore you are in New York." Of the latter type, an example might be "If someone takes 100 sleeping pills, he'll die; Joe took 100 sleeping pills, so Joe is going to die."—rather depressing example of a logical argument. We might refute one or the other of the premises in either of these syllogism examples, but in and of themselves, the arugments are perfectly valid logically.

A common fallacy in syllogisms is that of denying the antecedent. An example is the following argument: "If you commit a federal offense, you'll go to prison. You did not commit a federal offense. Therefore you will not go to prison." Certainly not absolutely true; there are plenty of non-Federal crimes you might commit, ending up in prison. This kind of argument can be twisted around if the antecedent is negative. "If John was not near the grocery store last night, he must have been home. John was near the store, so he couldn't have been at home." What if his home is two doors down from the grocery store? This argument also contains a lack of clarity in the exact meaning of the word "near." Lawyers especially ought to recognize this kind of illogic!

Another fallacy in syllogisms occurs in the disjunctive type. We might say, for example, that you must either leave the country or risk arrest for a crime you are accused of. You leave the country. Therefore you do not get arrested. This argument is fallacious; you might get arrested even if you leave the country. It could be that you might get arrested anyplace you went because you had committed a Federal crime. This fallacy arises from confusion between the inclusive (most usual) and exclusive forms of disjunction.

Sometimes it's fun to use ridiculous statements in demonstrating logical validity. This eliminates the tendency to assign our own ideas about everyday life to logical arguments. If the moon is made of Swiss cheese, then ants prefer to eat caviar. The moon is made of Swiss cheese. Thus, ants prefer to eat caviar. This is logically sound. If we deny the antecedent, we might argue that because the moon is not made of Swiss chesse, ants will not prefer caviar. Well, I'm not an ant, and I wouldn't know; but I'll bet hungry ants would swarm all over a bowl of caviar if it were made avilable to them.

Either Mars is inhabited by little green men who reproduce by budding (there aren't any little green women), or the sky appears blue as seen from the surface of the earth on a clear day. Mars has no little green men who reproduce by budding. Therefore, the sky is blue as seen from the surface of the earth on a clear day. This illustrates another fallacy, and that is an occurrence where the first statement in a syllogism is always true. It proves absolutely nothing. If there were little green men on Mars who reproduce by budding, the sky would still be blue as seen from the surface of the earth on a clear day. But subtly we might be able to convince someone that the two events were connected and green men on Mars would have something to do with the color of the sky here. The argument is fallacious, but it is often done.

CONTRADICTION

If a contradiction occurs in logic, it follows that anything is possible. This may be written as $X(-X) \rightarrow Y$, where X and Y might be any statements whatever. When a mathematical theory falls upon itself in this way, or any statement is made that contradicts itself, anything follows. If you contradict yourself with me, I'll tell you the moon is made of Swiss cheese and there are little green men on Mars who reproduce by budding. If you deny it, you'll be right; if you agree with me, you'll be right then, too!

Table 2-6 illustrates the logical implication function. We can prove that a contradiction results in anything by means of a simple truth table, as shown at Table 2-7. A theorem results when the conclusion is always true. $X(-X) \rightarrow Y$ is always true, regardless of the truth values of X and Y. Truth in fact loses meaning in case of a contradiction. A whole complicated theory will collapse and cease to exist, if just one little contradiction is found.

REDUCTIO AD ABSURDUM

An interesting method of proving a theorem is to demonstrate that its denial results in a contradiction. If we wish to prove X, for example, we begin by assuming $-X$, and argue, step by step, until a contradiction is reached. A contradiction takes the form $Y(-Y)$, where Y might be anything. This method of logical proof by deduction is called *reductio ad absurdum*, meaning "reduced to meaninglessness."

Let us say, for example, that we wish to prove that $(xy)z = x(yz)$ for all real numbers x, y, and z.

X	Y	$X \rightarrow Y$
0	0	1
0	1	1
1	0	0
1	1	1

Table 2-6. Truth Table for the Implication (If-Then) Logical Function. An If-Then Statement Is True Unless the Antecedent Is True and the Conclusion Is False.

Table 2-7. Truth-Table Demonstration that the Statement $X(-X) \rightarrow Y$ Is Always True, and Is Therefore a Theorem, Regardless of the Truth Value of Y.

X	$-X$	$X(-X)$	Y	$X(-X) \rightarrow Y$
1	0	0	0	1
0	1	0	1	1

This is known as the *associative law of multiplication*. To prove this, we might say that there exists some a, b, and c for which this is not true; that is, for the particular numbers a, b, and c, $(ab)c \neq a(bc)$. We need only one example of this to prove that the associative law is invalid. But if $(ab)c \neq a(bc)$, then $(axby)cz \neq axby(cz)$ for all x, y, and z. This follows because if $(ab)c \neq a(bc)$, then $(xyz)(ab)c \neq (xyz)a(bc)$, the product xyz being the same on both sides of the inequality. We can choose x, y, and z such that ax, by, and cz may be any real numbers whatsoever. So then the associative law would be false for all real numbers ax, by, and cz. We can easily show that this is nonsense; let $ax = 1$, $by = 2$, and $cz = 3$. Then it is easy to demonstrate that the associative law holds for these numbers. We have now proven that the associative law is false for all real numbers, yet is true for 1, 2, and 3. This is a contradiction. Thus, the assumption that the associative law is invalid is a false assumption, and we are forced to accept that the associative law is valid for all real numbers.

This kind of reasoning is not always necessary, and is not always the easiest way to prove a theorem. You may have to read over the previous paragraph a few times in order to grasp the reasoning process. When you do understand the process, it may seem ridiculous (literally meaning worthy of ridicule) to go to such lengths to prove that which is so obvious. But in mathematics, nothing is obvious until it is proven—not shown to be probably true, or likely true, or even almost certainly true—but true beyond the slightest bit of doubt.

INDUCTIVE LOGIC

Inductive logic takes two forms. One is a form of deductive logic, which will not be discussed here, execpt to say that it is often used to prove theorems for the set of natural numbers or integers. We might say that if some fact is true for any integer n, then it is true for $n + 1$; thus it is true for all integers greater than or equal to n. A simple example is to say that if n and m are integers, then $n + m$ is an integer also.

The other form of inductive logic is called, on occasion, "lawyers' logic." We prove in inductive reasoning that something is probably true. The problem comes in when we attempt to define the meaning of *probably.* We can, at one extreme, insist that something almost certainly be true in order to be "probably" true; at the other extreme we might say that any probability of more than 50 percent constitutes sufficient grounds for that conclusion.

If we see rain coming down, it is almost certainly true that the sky is at least partly cloudy. (There may be exceptions, but I haven't seen any.) We might say that it's probably true that the sky is at least 50 percent clouded. It is almost certainly true that the sky is 15 percent clouded. But how probable is it that it is completely overcast? I have seen plenty of downpours when clear sky was visible.

Inductive logic can be demonstrated by example. We may toss a die and say, after several thousand tosses, that the chances are five out of six that we will not get a roll of one. In fact, by statistics, unless the die is loaded we know that the chances of this are exactly five out of six. But every die is at least a little bit loaded. The distribution of the plastic is not perfect on account of imperfections in the manufacturing process.

Inductive logic is so inexact that we should classify it as philosophy and not strict mathematics. Here is a rather odd example. Suppose the speed limit on a particular stretch of highway is 55 miles per hour. This might mean that you are speeding if you go over 55, or it might mean (if some officer needs to meet a quota badly enough) that you are speeding if you go 55 or more. Now suppose you are cruising along at 54.6 miles per hour and the police radar reads the speed to only two digits, rounding it off to 55. The officer may think you were "probably" speeding; after all, you might have been going 55.2 miles per hour and the radar would still show 55. Thus you are stopped and perhaps ticketed for speeding when you were in fact not speeding. The probability of your speeding is exactly 50 percent in such a case, your speed in theory being any real number x such that $54.5 < x < 55.5$ if the radar rounds to two digits and shows 55. If we round off 50 percent, or 0.5, to the nearest whole digit, that digit is by custom 1; this means that, by a twisted form of reasoning, a reading of 55 on radar means the chances are 100 percent that you are going more than 55 miles per hour! Inductive logic can sometimes be wrong. What is probably true might in fact be false, producing a ridiculous or frivolous conclusion such as the one just derived here.

FOUNDATIONS: THE SEARCH

Around the turn of the century, many changes were taking place in the scientific community. Physics, which had apparently become an exact science with little or nothing left to be discovered in order for it to become a perfect tautology, was shaken by Albert Einstein's theory of relativity. The notion of absoluteness in space was reduced to meaninglessness. At about the same time, a similar crisis was taking place in the mathematical world. It was almost like an earthquake: the very ground of knowledge seemed to be no longer solid.

Logic was, and by many still is, thought to be basic and central to mathematics, as mathematics is basic and central to all science. But the noted logician and philosopher Bertrand Russell put all this aside—and shook the confidence of the mathematician in his ivory tower of security—by proving a theorem that said, in effect, that we can define a set that cannot exist. This is the famous Russell Paradox. It runs somewhat parallel with the notion of incompleteness put forth by Kurt Gödel: in some logical environments, there are statements the truth value of which cannot be known. We would like to think that once we have defined something, then it, in at least some intuitive sense, exists. We would also feel comfortable knowing that any given statement has truth value either 0 (false) or 1 (true) based on a known set of axioms. Unfortunately, neither of these "pretty" things is the case unless the theory is constructed so as to result in a contradiction somewhere, pulling the stops and reducing the theory to nonsense.

It is one thing to have the idea of the physical universe be so complex as to be out of reach. Some say that God designed the universe that way on purpose, or say that we are too weak, not yet far enough advanced, to grasp all of the aspects of an infinitely sophisticated cosmos. But to think that thought itself is beyond thought—and that is unacceptable! Are we no more than furry little animals running around in some space-time singularity that we are not even qualified or capable to think about?

The mathematician Gottlob Frege was working on a book in which he endeavored to base all of arithmetic on set theory. Numbers can in fact be defined in terms of sets. Zero is defined as the set containing the null (empty) set, and 1 is defined as the set containing the null set and zero; then 2 is defined as the set containing the null set and 1, and so on. At least this is one way to do it:

$$0 = \{\phi\}$$
$$1 = \{\phi, 0\} = \{\phi, \{\phi\}\}$$
$$2 = \{\phi, 1\} = \{\phi, \{\phi, \{\phi\}\}\}$$

On this basis, all of the whole numbers are constructed, for once we know a given whole number n, we can define $n + 1$ as $\{\phi, n\}$. From these, the negative numbers are made as a mirror image. From these come the rational numbers, and with operations such as roots, logarithms, and exponential functions, all of the real numbers arise.

Russell brought his paradox, which shook the foundations of set theory, to the attention of Frege just as he was completing his work. If Russell was right, the entire world of mathematics was in great danger of collapsing into a contradictory, meaningless, trivial bit of whimsy. Had all this work been done for nothing? Without mathematics, there could be no science with any solid validity. Gödel's Incompleteness Theorem compounded the problem. If there were certain things the truth value of which could not be determined, then there were mysteries of the universe that could not be solved. In fact the incompleteness problem has never been totally resolved, and the crisis in set theory has given rise to various different philosophies concerning how mathematics, the fundamental basis of all our scientific knowledge, ought to be handled.

It would seem that the universe has characteristics that cause it to be either infinitely complicated or else meaningless. For if we allow for truth and falsity to be different and separate, there are "gaps" that can't be filled, and if we insist that the gaps be filled, all knowledge loses its significance. We must accept that there is too much in this cosmos for us to ever know—or else that there is nothing here at all.

Chapter 3

What's the Limit?

One of the most peculiar aspects of mathematics involves the theory of limits. Limits are a particular aspect of a branch of mathematics called *analysis*, which concerns functions and their characteristics. This all sounds pretty complicated, and it can get very involved, but it is not necessary to go into analysis very far in order to get some strange results.

How fast can a person run a mile, for example? For a long time it was thought that nobody would ever run a mile in less than four minutes, but finally someone did. Now they talk occasionally about a three-minute mile. Everyone agrees that it will be a long time, if ever, before someone runs a mile in less than three minutes. It is probably universally agreed that no two-minute mile will ever be run; and a one-minute mile is ridiculous to even speculate about. Or is it?

There is a limit to how fast one can run a mile—an exact limit. The same holds for all sporting events, such as how fast a human can swim 100 meters freestyle or how far a man can hit a baseball. There is a limit to the speed attainable by means of space-ship propulsion. These are precise limits, real numbers. But we have absolutely no way of ever knowing exactly what they are. We are thus faced with the odd paradox of knowing that an exact value exists, and also knowing that we can never find out what it is.

LIMITS

Some functions increase or decrease without limit, or reach a definite value and stay there. Some functions, however, can increase all the time and never go past a certain value, or decrease continuously and never get less a certain value. Two examples are shown in Fig. 3-1. At A, the positive part of the function $f(x) = 1/x$ is shown. This function decreases toward zero as the value of x increases. No matter how large x gets, the value of $f(x)$ remains positive, although it never quite gets down to zero. However, for any x_2 greater than x_1, $f(x_2) < f(x_1)$, regardless of how large or small x_1 and x_2 are on a relative scale. At B, the function $f(x) = -1/x$ is shown for positive values of x. This function is always negative and increases toward

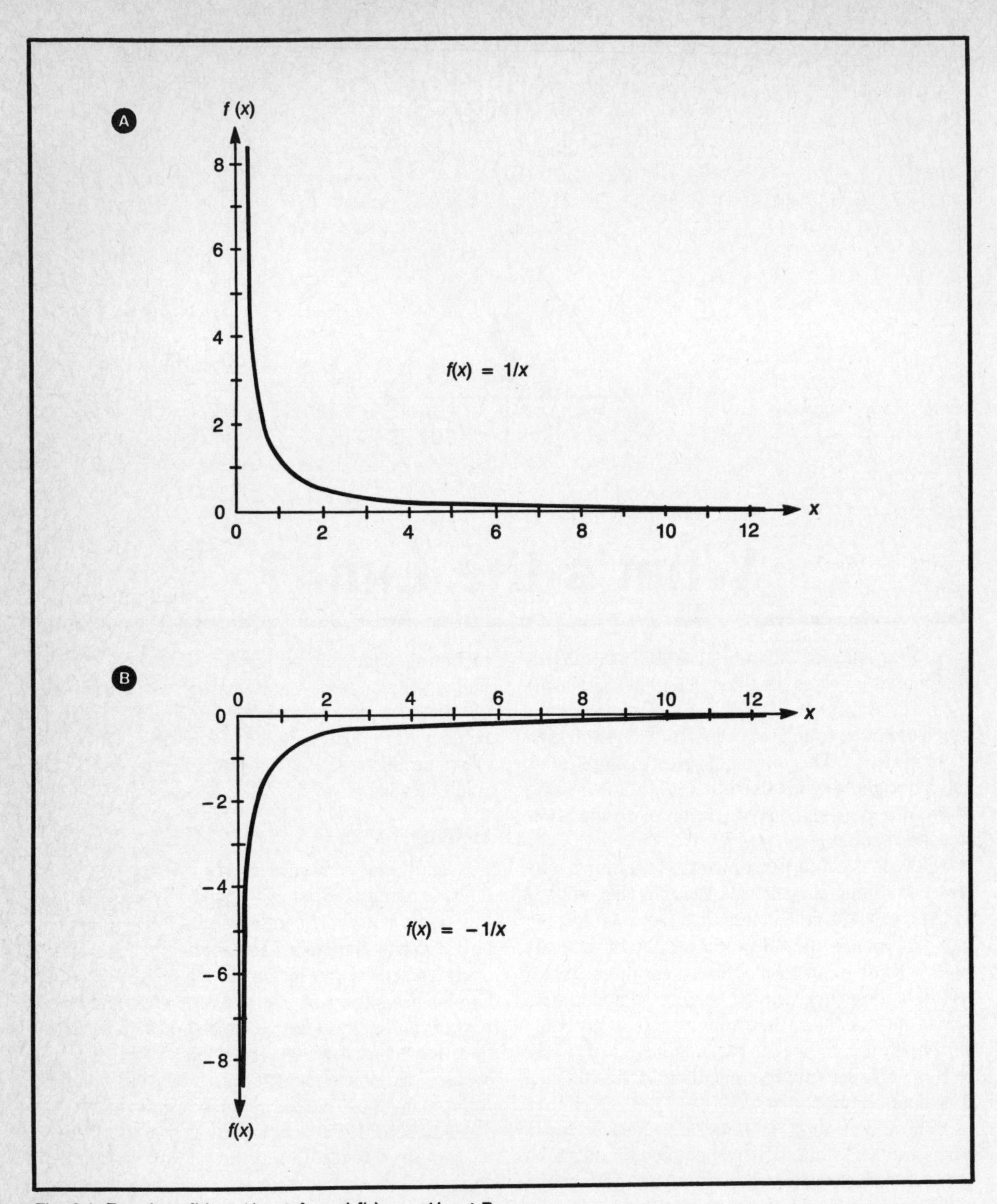

Fig. 3-1. Functions $f(x) = 1/x$, at A, and $f(x) = -1/x$, at B.

zero as the value of x increases. But no matter how large x may be, the value of $f(x)$ remains less than zero. For any x_1 and x_2 such that $x_1 < x_2$, it is true that $f(x_1) < f(x_2)$.

These are examples of functions that are continuous—that is, there are no breaks in them—and always decreasing or increasing, yet having limiting values, in both cases zero. An analogy can be made to the frog that jumps half of the way to a wall, over and over and over. The frog never reaches the wall but gets a little bit closer with every jump.

Some functions increase without limit. An example of this kind of function is the positive portion of the parabola $f(x) = x^2$; another is the function $f(x) = \log_{10}(x)$. Both of these examples are illustrated at Fig. 3-2 A and B. In these cases, there is no limit to how large $f(x)$ can get as the value of x increases. There is no upper bound.

A function that increases and never gets beyond a certain point is said to have an upper bound. Similarly, a function that decreases and never attains a value less than a certain amount is said to have a lower bound. Shortly we will see that any function having an upper or lower bound has a unique value that can define this boundary point.

FUNCTIONS THAT BLOW UP

Some functions approach a limit in a different way: the ordinate, or value of the function, "blows up" at a certain point or points. In Fig. 3-1, the function "blows up" at the value $x = 0$; at this point in either A or B, the function value $f(x)$ is undefined. This occurs also at B of Fig. 3-2. It is not sufficient to say that the value of the function is "infinity" or "negative infinity" at these points. We will delve more into the meaning of infinity—or at least one interpretation of it—later in this book.

A good example of a function that "blows up" infinitely at many points is the tangent function (Fig. 3-3). This function is undefined at any value that is an odd integral multiple of 90 degrees. The function skyrockets up as the value of x increases toward 90 degrees, and then disappears altogether at 90 degrees, only to come zooming up from the far negative as the value of x gets past 90 degrees. At 180 degrees the value passes through zero, and then repeats its upward journey and disappears again at 270 degrees.

No matter how close we get to an undefined point in a "blowup" type function such as this, the value $f(x)$ always is finite. Using my calculator I find that the value tan(89) = 57.28996163 to 10 significant digits. Now I find tan(89.9) = 572.9572134. Going closer, I find that the value tan(89.99) = 5729.577893. It appears that with each additional digit 9 after the decimal for x, tan(x) increases about tenfold. If I enter 89.99999999 into my calculator, I get 5729577951 as the result. When I put 90 into the calculator I get "E" for "error." Of course the calculator is a digital device and has its limitations as to how far it can be pushed. But in theory, we could enter 89.999. . . with perhaps a quadrillion 9's after the decimal point, and still the tangent would be defined—although it would be an incomprehensibly large number.

A "blowup" point in a function is sometimes called an *asymptote*. The asymptote is the value x for which the function is not defined. There may be no asymptotes in a function, or one, or several, or many, even infinitely many, as is the case with the tangent function. Sometimes the asymptote point has the function going in opposite directions, as in Fig. 3-3, or it might be in the same direction on either side of the asymptote, as shown in Fig. 3-4, where the function is defined as $f(x) = 1/x$ if $x > 0$ and $f(x) = -1/x$ if $x < 0$.

THE THEOREM OF LEAST UPPER BOUND

If a function is bounded above, that is, it never exceeds a certain value, then this value is unique. Stated another way, if y is some value of the ordinate in a coordinate system such that $y > f(x)$ for every abscissa x, then y is an upper bound of f, and there exists some unique ordinate y^* that represents the least upper bound of f. It will be true that, for all x, $f(x) < y^*$, but for any y less than y^*, there will exist some x such that $y = f(x)$. (The function might also be bounded from below, so this might be only locally true.)

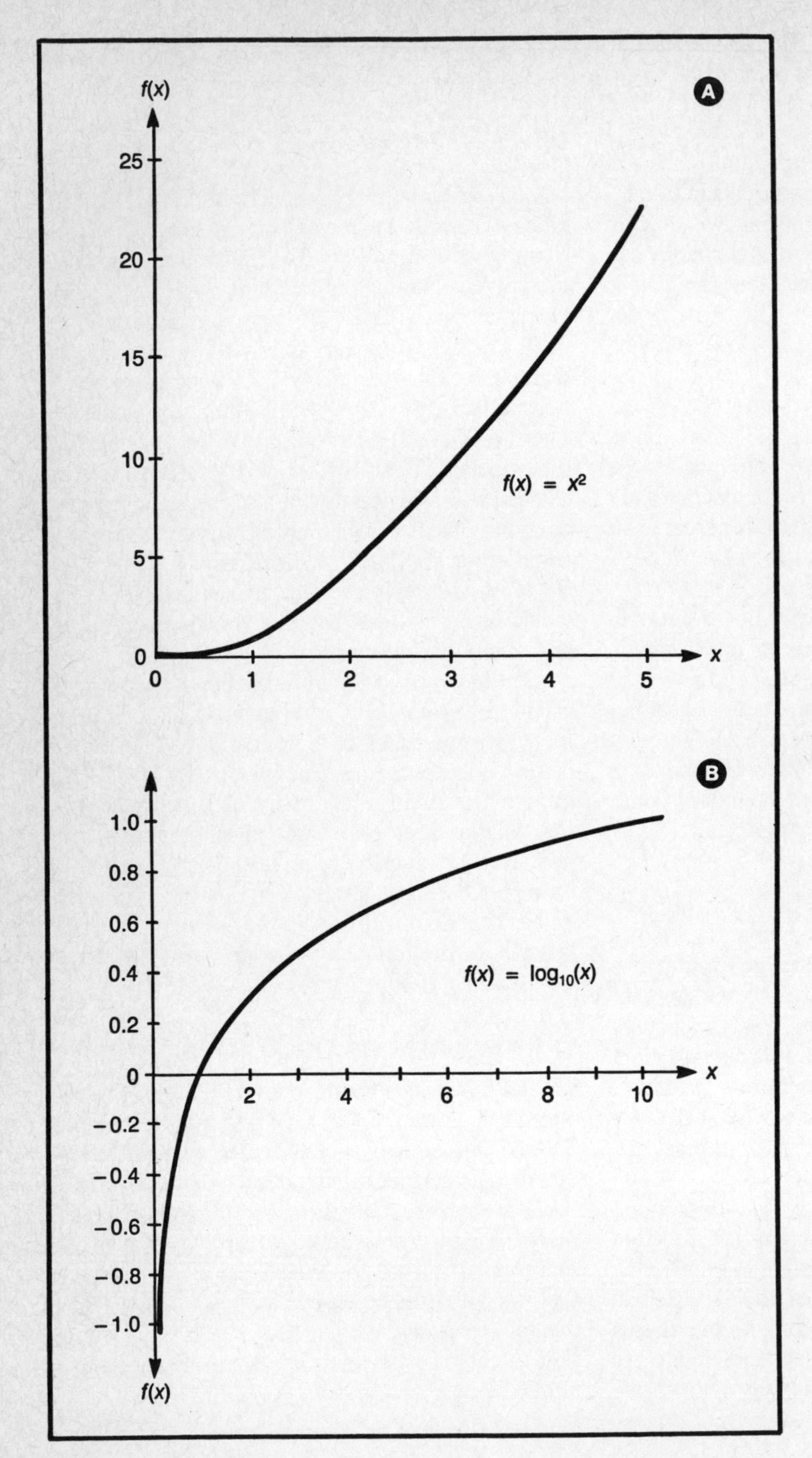

Fig. 3-2. At A, the parabola $f(x) = x^2$; at B, the logarithmic function, $f(x) = \log_{10}(x)$.

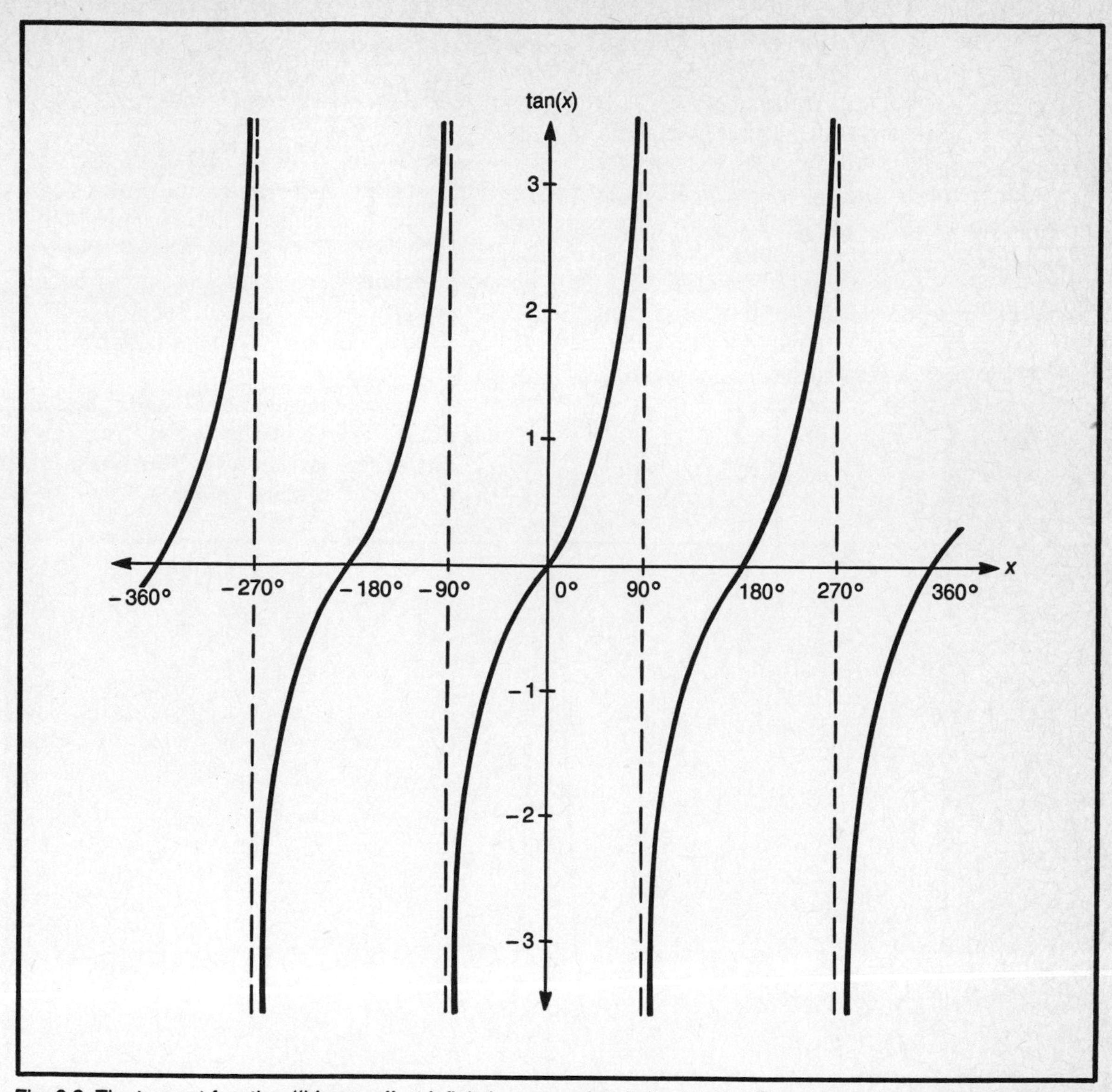

Fig. 3-3. The tangent function "blows up" at infinitely many points in its domain. These occur in opposite directions at every point.

We return to the example of Fig. 3-1B, where $f(x) = -1/x$ for $x > 0$. In this case $y^* = 0$. Any positive number is an upper bound of f, because $f(x)$ is never positive. Any negative number is part of the range of f; that is, if $y < 0$ then there is some x such that $f(x) = y$. Therefore zero is the least upper bound of this function. In order to show that a number is a least upper bound, we must show that any number (locally) less than this number will be a part of the range of the function, and that any number greater than this number will not be a part of the range of the function. The least upper bound itself may or may not be a part of the range. In the case of Fig. 3-1B, zero is not part of the range. However, it might be in a function such as $f(x) = x-1$ if $x < 1$ and $f(x) = 0$ if $x > 1$. This is shown in

Fig. 3-5. The least upper bound is zero, just as is the case for the function at Fig. 3-1B; however zero is part of the function in the example of Fig. 3-5.

If you have ever taken a course in analysis at the high-school level or higher, then you have heard of the theorems of least upper bound and greatest lower bound. These theorems are actually mirror images of each other. If a function is bounded above, there is a least upper bound, and if it is bounded below, there is a greatest lower bound. The least upper bound or greatest lower bound are unique numbers. It may or may not be possible to determine what the values actually are.

Theorem. If S is a set of real numbers, not empty, having an upper bound, then there is a unique real number y^* that represents the least upper bound of the set S. This is true for sets in general, or for sets representing the ranges of functions $f(x) = y$.

Proof: Define S^* as the set of all real numbers representing upper bounds of the set S. Because we have assumed that the function is bounded above, S^* is not empty. Define S^{**} as the set of all real numbers that are not upper bounds of S. Now let y be a member of set S. Then $y - 1$ is in S^{**}, since this value cannot possibly be an upper bound of S.

Let y_1 be some member of S^{**} and y_2 be some member of S^*. Then it is true that $y_1 < y_2$. This is true because there is some w in S such that $y_1 < w$. However, $w < y_2$ since y_2 is in S^*.

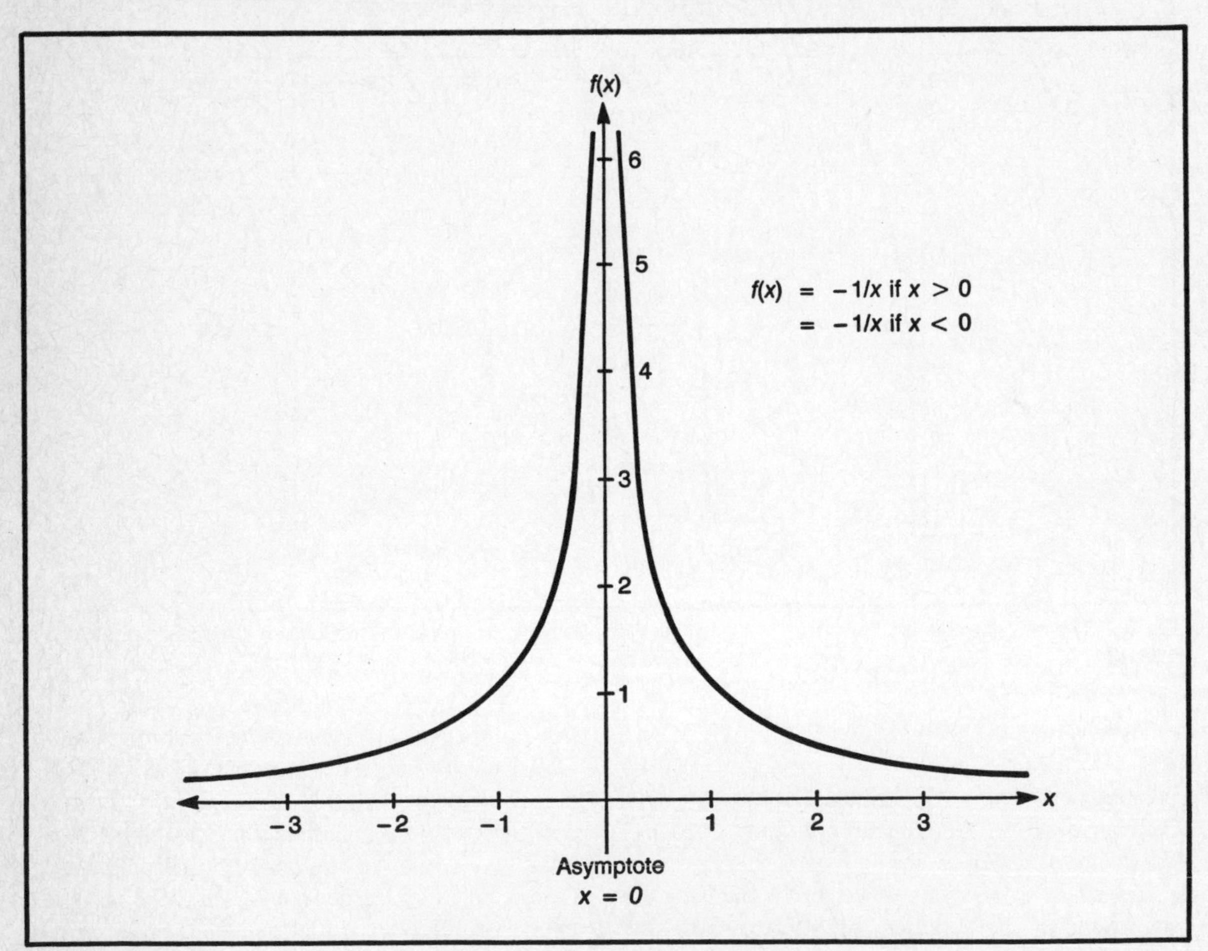

Fig. 3-4. An example of a function that "blows up" in the same direction on both sides of a single point in its domain.

There is a unique number y^* that is either the largest member of S^* or the smallest member of S^{**}. If $y^* < y_1$ then y^* is in S^*. Thus, y^* is not in S^{**}, because if this were true, there would be some w in S with $y^* < w$.

Suppose $v = (y^* + w)/2$, putting v in between y^* and w. (The number v is the arithmetic mean or average of y^* and w.) Then v must be in S^*, since $y^* < v$. But v is in S^{**} also, since $v < w$. This is a contradiction, since S^* and S^{**} are disjoint sets. Assuming that y^* can be in S^{**} leads to this contradiction. Because y^* must be either in S^{**} or S^*, we know it is in S^*, and must be the smallest member thereof. Thus, y^* is a unique number that is the least upper bound of S.

The foregoing case is illustrated generally in Fig. 3-6.

This proof is based on the notion that a set is open-ended above, that is, approaches the upper bound but never actually reaches it. If the set is closed above, the upper bound is simply the largest member of the set. This is the case with the function in Fig. 3-5.

The theorem for greatest lower bound is a mirror image of the foregoing, and we need not prove that here since it would be repetitive. If a set has a lower bound, then there exists a unique number representing the greatest lower bound. In Fig. 3-1A, the greatest lower bound is zero. This is also true of the functions in Figs. 3-2A and 3-4.

THE FASTEST MILE

The theorems of least upper bound and greatest lower bound have many practical consequences that are quite startling. A good example occurs in the case of the mile run, and there are countless other situations in which similar limiting conditions exist. In fact, some aspect of either of

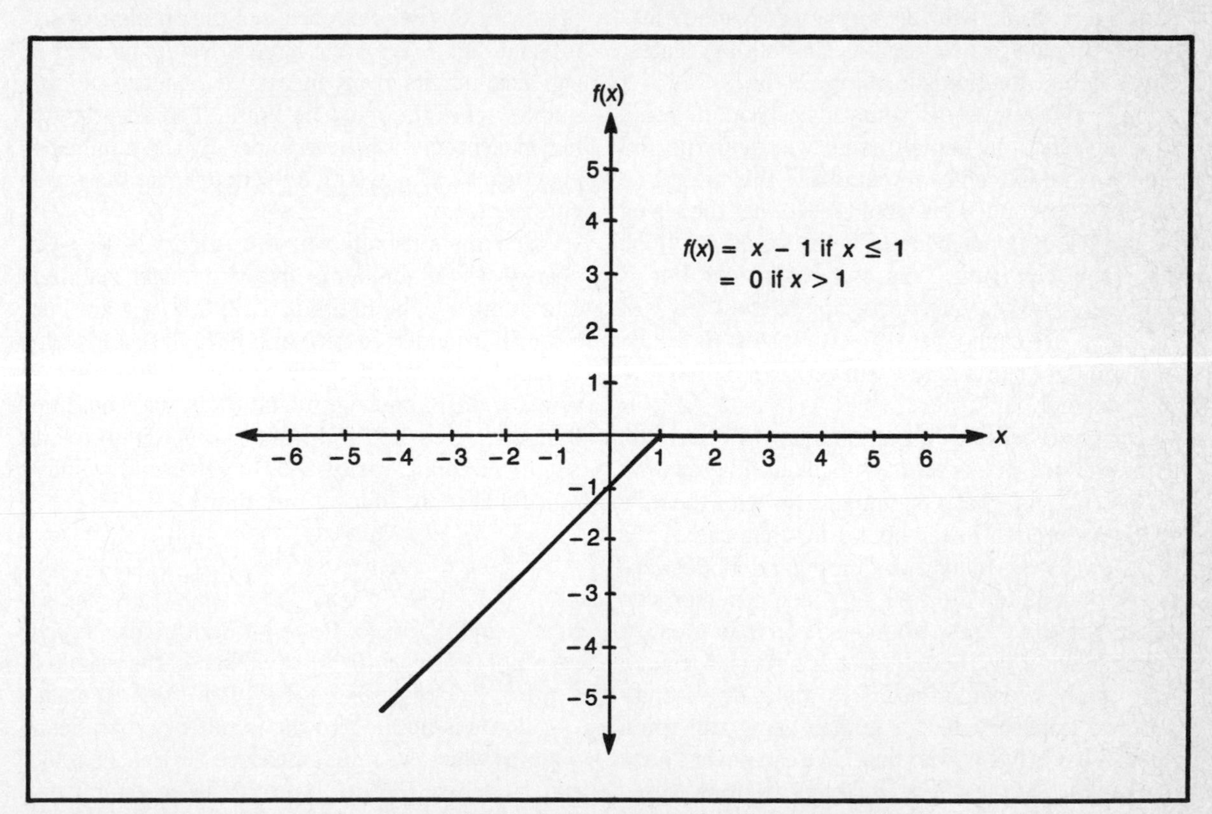

Fig. 3-5. An example of a function that reaches its limiting value rather than approaching it.

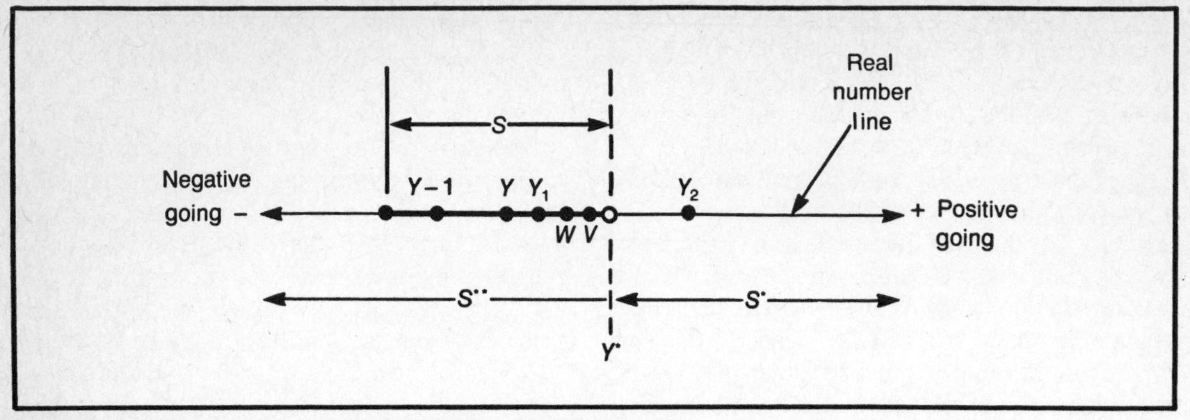

Fig. 3-6. Illustration of the proof of the theorem of least upper bound.

these theorems is likely to be involved in almost every aspect of real life.

For many years it was thought that no one would ever run a mile in less than four minutes. This barrier was being approached, but people doubted it would ever be surpassed. Nonetheless it was, proving that four minutes is not the greatest lower bound for times in the mile run.

Yet there must be some lower bound, some time in which no human being will ever run the mile. In the extreme we could say this would be 1/186,282 second. This would mean that the speed of light is an upper bound for the speed at which a person can run. This is nonsensical but it definitely is true, even according to the theory of relativity. We cannot deny that the fastest time anyone will ever run a mile is slower than 5.36821×10^{-6} second.

Even to believe that any human will ever run a one-minute mile is pretty ridiculous. We can say with confidence that a one-minute time for the mile run represents a lower bound for that event.

Now having found two times that doubtless are lower bounds for the time in which a person can run the mile, we know from the theorem of greatest lower bound that there in fact is a barrier time, a time that represents the fastest time, or an unattainable time, in which a human being can run a mile. What is this barrier time? We can never know. We might suppose it is 3:24.334 (that is, three minutes, 24.334 seconds). But doubtless we would get a time less than that someday; there are so many variables such as altitude, wind direction and speed, the condition of the track, and even the kind of tread on the running shoes! Someone would prove this barrier invalid by going 3:24.3334. That brings up another complication: the problem of significant digits. We must have a certain number of significant digits in any measured quantity, and this number of digits must be finite. The accuracy of our measurement is determined by the number of significant digits to which we determine that measurement.

Scientists usually round off digits so that the nearest whole number is obtained for the last digit in a number. The digits 0, 1, 2, 3, and 4 are customarily rounded to zero and 5, 6, 7, 8, and 9 are rounded to 1. Thus, if we have 0.54 and want to round it off to one significant digit, we would get 0.5; if we have 0.56 and want to round it off to one significant digit, we get 0.6. In general, if we have a decimal point followed by digits

$$x.n_1n_2n_3 \ldots n_{m-1}n_m,$$

then rounding off to the $m-1$ digit gives $x.n_1n_2n_3 \ldots n_{m-1}$ if n_m is 0, 1, 2, 3, or 4; the result is $x.n_1n_2n_3 \ldots (n_{m-1} + 1)$ if n_m is 5, 6, 7, 8, or 9.

There is no limit to the number of significant digits to which we might measure the time of a mile run. So all we have to do to break an established barrier is measure the time to more significant digits, and sooner or later the barrier, established as a rational number to only a certain number of significant digits, will be broken. A definite barrier *cannot* be determined for the mile run, because it would have an infinite number of significant digits! We would therefore not be capable of reading out the digital display, even if an instrument could be built that would contain an infinitely long digital display.

We can prove this informally by supposing that we have a display that shows $x.n_1n_2n_3 \ldots .n_m$, where m is the number of digits to the right of the decimal point. It is clear that m is an integer. The chances of n_{m+1} being exactly zero are just one in ten. The chances of n_{m+2} and n_{m+1} both being exactly zero are one in 100. The chances of all the digits n_i where $i > m$ being zero are infinitely small, that is $0.1 \times 0.1 \times 0.1 \times \ldots$. It is inevitable that there will be some digits down the line that are not zero, no matter how far we go, no matter how large we care to make m.

Although our theorem says that there must be a greatest lower bound to the time in which a mile can be run, we are also aware that whatever this bound is, we can never find out precisely its value.

THE FASTEST 100-METER SWIM

A similar example can be found in the swimming event, perhaps the most exciting (at least to me) of international competition, the 100-meter freestyle event. Early in this century, it was thought ridiculous that anyone would ever go faster than 50 seconds in this swimming competition. In 1972, Mark Spitz swam it in 51.22 seconds, at that time an amazing speed. But in 1976 Jim Montgomery broke 50 seconds and went 49.99, followed by Jonty Skinner in 49.44 a few weeks after that. The imagined 50-second barrier was gone. (It's interesting to note that we tend to choose whole numbers as barriers for psychological reasons, without any basis in fact.)

The same reasoning applies here as in the mile run. What is the fastest time that one can possibly swim 100 meters? Certainly it is more than, say, one second flat. That is ridiculous; human reflexes are such that the swimmer doesn't even hit the water at the start until more time than that has gone by. So there is a lower bound. Perhaps Jonty Skinner would have gone 49.43 had he not trimmed his fingernails for a month before the swim, or had the electricity been of a different frequency in the timing devices. We never know what his true time was, anyway, and it doesn't matter, because people have swum 100 meters freestyle faster than 49.44 since that time.

Whatever the fastest mile time, whatever the fastest 100-meter swim time possible, we know that there is a barrier. This is shown in the diagrams of Fig. 3-7A and B, where the mile-run and 100-meter-swim times are shown as a function of the year of the race, the points indicating the fastest time that year. The dotted lines show the greatest lower bounds. These bounds are irrational numbers—that is, they cannot be exactly represented as decimal values—and are times that can be approached but not surpassed.

THE FASTEST POSSIBLE SPEED

According to the special theory of relativity, it is not possible for a material object to be accelerated to the speed of light. This happens because the mass of an object increases as the velocity increases. If, at rest, an object has mass m, then its mass at speed v is

$$m^* = \frac{1}{\sqrt{1 - (v^2/c^2)}}$$

where m^* is the mass at speed v, and c is the speed of light in the same units as v. The increase in mass as v approaches c is without an upper limit, as shown by the graph in Fig. 3-8.

The increase in mass is not apparent to passengers on a high-speed spaceship (No spaceship devised by humans has yet gone fast enough for the mass increase to be significant anyhow.) However, it is a real increase insofar as propulsion is concerned. The momentum of the spaceship increases along with the mass, in direct proportion to the velocity and the mass increase multiplied by each other. It takes more and more propulsive force—

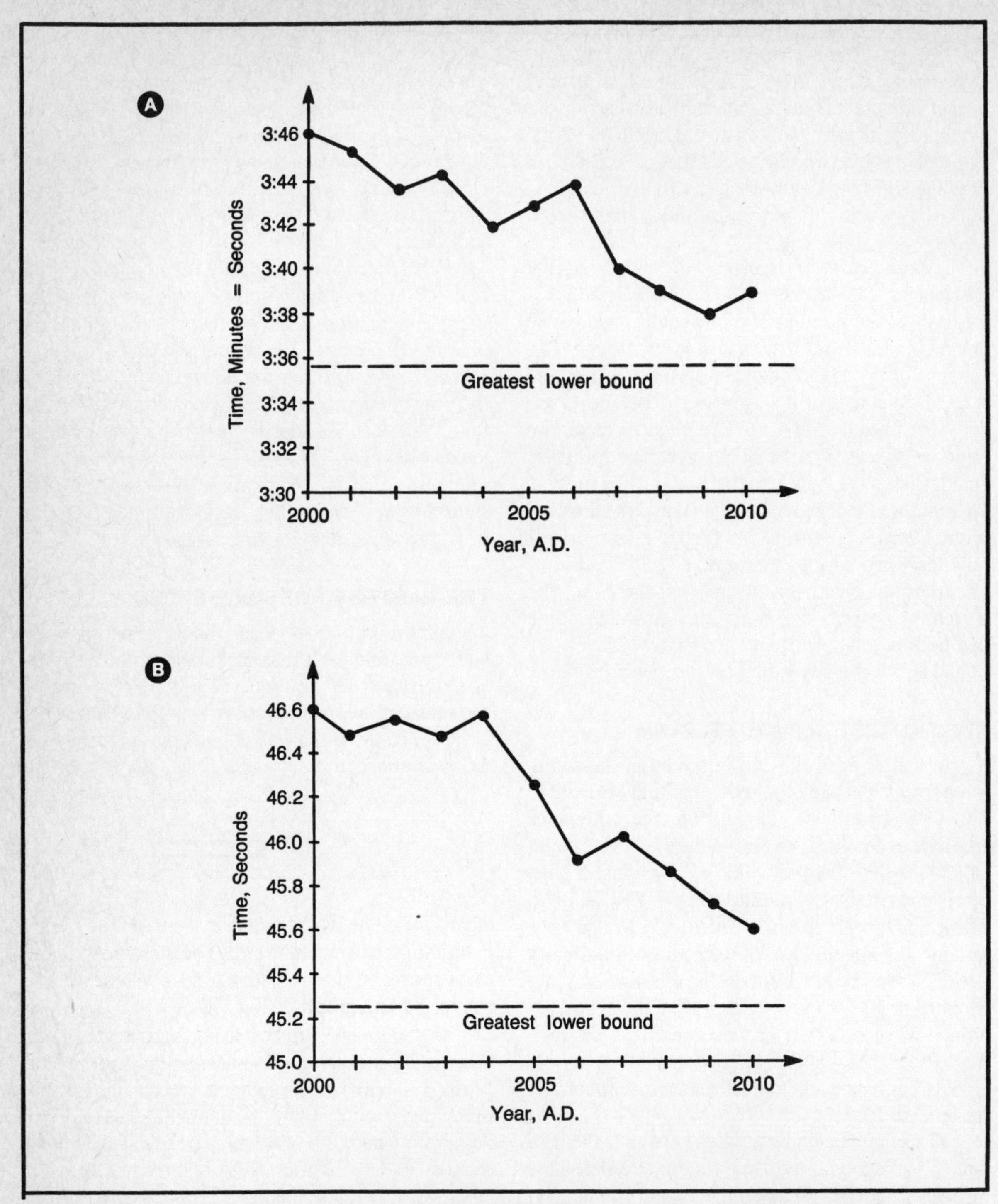

Fig. 3-7. At A, a hypothetical example of times for the mile run versus year. At B, a hypothetical example of times for the 100-meter swim versus year. In both cases, the greatest lower bound for time is shown, again hypothetically, by dotted lines.

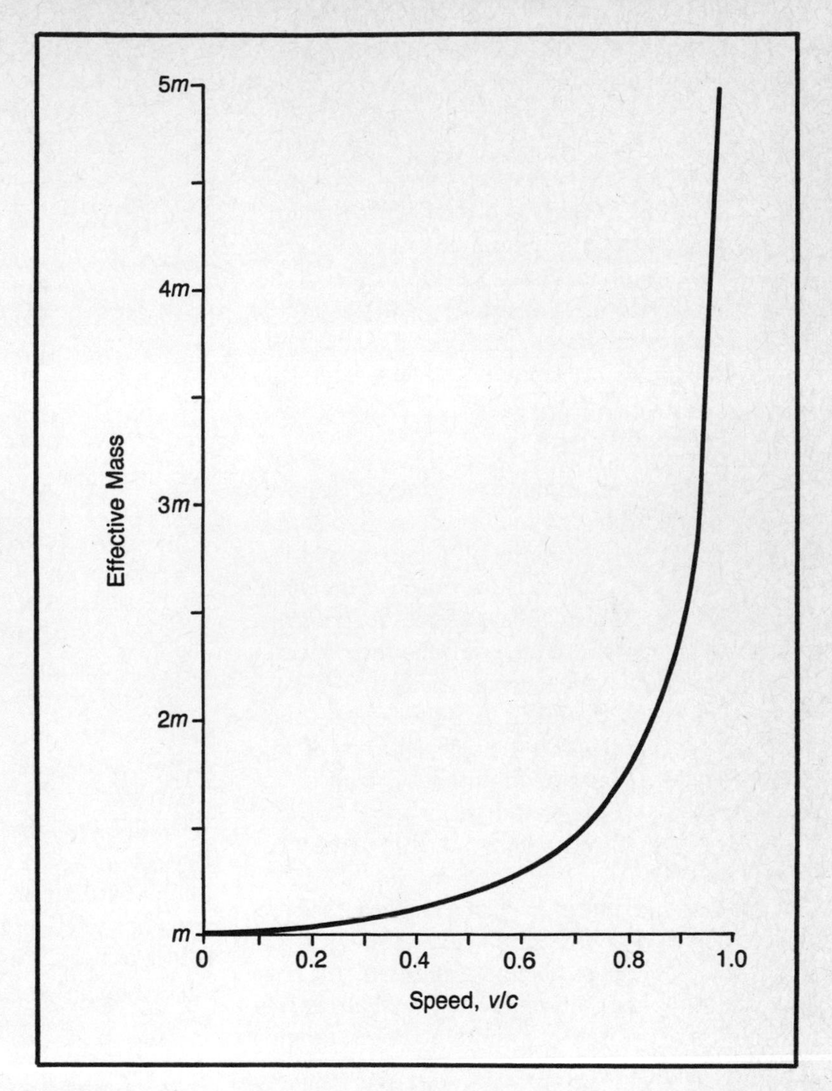

Fig. 3-8. The function of mass increase versus speed v/c. This function "blows up" when $v/c = 1$.

thrust—to get an increase of, say, one mile per hour as the velocity approaches the speed of light. No finite amount of fuel can allow the ship to reach or surpass c. This can be mathematically proven, but should be obvious enough intuitively since the function at Fig. 3-8 "blows up" at c.

Actually, the greatest speed achievable by any given means of propulsion is somewhat less than c. The speed of light represents an upper bound, and theoretically c is the least upper bound for speeds attainable by space vehicles. In practice the upper bound would have to be less than c because of physical constraints such as the need to carry fuel (that would be used up before a certain speed v^* could be reached). Even if the spaceship were able to gather up interstellar or intergalactic matter and use that as fuel for propulsion, there would be some resistance because of the gathering apparatus, and a limit to the amount of available interstellar or intergalactic matter. An infinite amount of thrust would be required to get to the speed of light, and even all the matter in the whole universe would not be enough for that.

So what is the fastest attainable speed? Again, as with the mile run and the 100-meter freestyle swim, we can never know exactly. It is some irrational fraction of the speed of light. The speed, v^*, representing the fastest possible speed with any particular means of propulsion, is such that $v/c = 0.n_1n_2n_3 \ldots$, where we can never predict, knowing the value of n_i, whether n_{i+1} is 0, 1, 2, 3, 4, 5, 6, 7, 8, or 9. We would need to conduct infinitely many experiments, using infinitely many different spaceship designs, having a device with a digital display having an infinite number of digits, and as if this is not prohibitive enough, each experiment would take an infinite amount of time to complete.

QUANTIZED SPACE?

We might get around the irrational-number problem, and all of the faults in a system that is represented by a continuum of infinite resolution, by postulating that space is quantized. This would mean that there is a smallest possible spatial interval in the real world. This might be the diameter of an elementary particle, whatever that is. (We will have more to say about the particle theory of matter in a later chapter.) The smallest interval of time would be the amount of time that is required for a photon, or particle of radiant energy, to travel from one end of the elementary particle to the other end (Fig. 3-9).

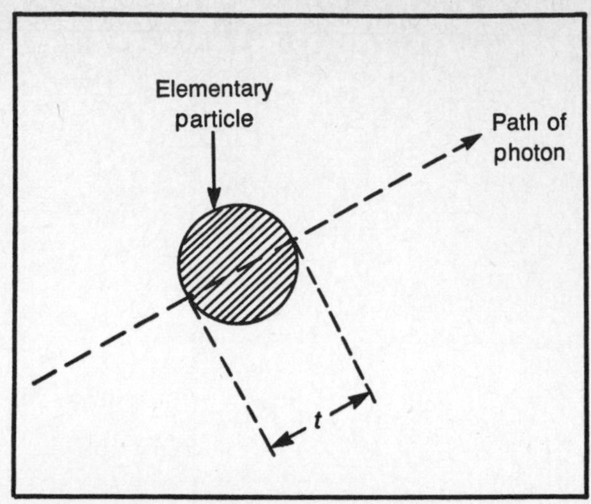

Fig. 3-9. Possible example of the shortest interval of time in the cosmos.

If space and time are in fact quantized, then any speed, distance or time can be expressed in terms of a rational number. Such a number might have many hundreds or thousands of decimal places, but it could be expressed in a finite number of digits. Then we could, at least theoretically, determine the fastest possible mile run or 100-meter freestyle or speed for a spaceship using a certain kind of propulsion. However, the experimentation might still require more time than we could ever muster. And, no doubt, someone would someday come along without trimming his or her nails prior to the big swim. Then the magnificent theorem might collapse in a split second.

The idea of quantized space relieves us of the worry that there might be an infinite hierarchy of particles, smaller and smaller, with no elementary constituent. If space is quantized, then one quantum is entirely taken up by the elementary particle. We have no idea what this particle might be as of today, because we are always finding new kinds of particles.

There is a possibility that elementary particles exist in the form of black holes, surrounded by spherical regions marking the boundaries within which gravitational singularity of space-time exists. We will have more to say about black holes later. But for now, we know only the law of the continuum: space is apparently capable of being split into finer and finer parts without limit, and the same is true of time. There is evidently no smallest possible spatial distance, and no shortest moment in time.

THE SLOPE OF A CURVE

In analysis, the slope of a straight line is defined as the ratio of the change in the dependent variable to the change in the independent variable. Several examples are shown in Fig. 3-10. Usually the slope is determined as

$$m = (y_2 - y_1)/(x_2 - x_1)$$

where (x_1,y_1) and (x_2,y_2) are two points on the line. The slope, m, may be determined using any two points, and in the case of a straight line, will always be the same as long as the two points are different. Positive slopes go up as you move toward the

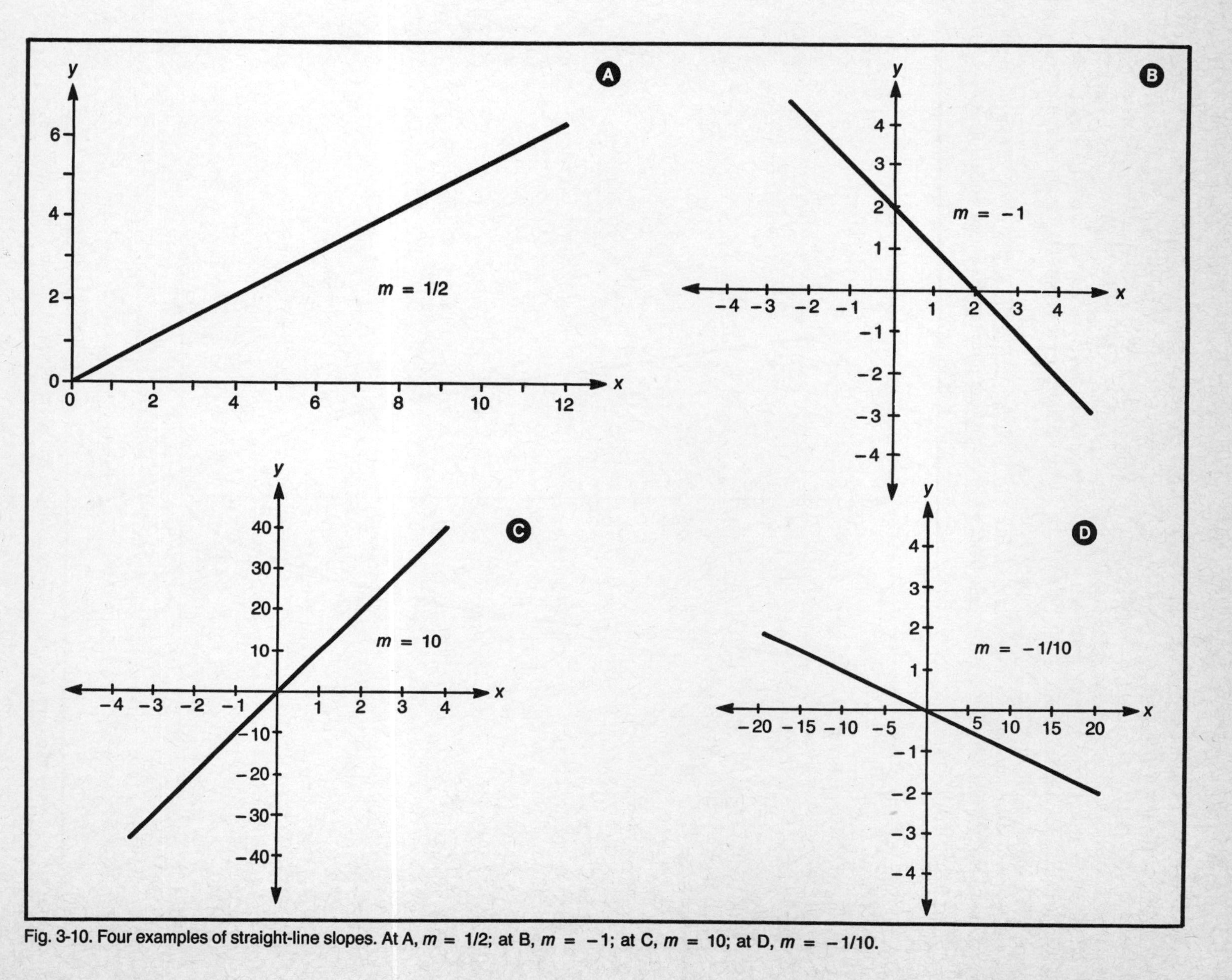

Fig. 3-10. Four examples of straight-line slopes. At A, $m = 1/2$; at B, $m = -1$; at C, $m = 10$; at D, $m = -1/10$.

right on the graph; negative slopes go down, as can be seen in the examples.

All lines have definite slopes, except for lines that run vertically. For these lines the slope is not defined because the denominator $(x_2 - x_1)$ is zero for any two points on the line.

For a curve, there is no definite slope. The slope varies depending on our choice of points. For some curves the slope is negative in some places and positive in other places. An example of this is the parabola $y = x^2$ (Fig. 3-11). When $x < 0$ the slope is negative, and when $x > 0$ it is positive. We might qualify this by saying that both x_1 and x_2 must be on the same side of zero (either both positive or both negative) for this to be true in every case.

We can define the slope of a curve at a certain point by defining the slope of a line tangent to the

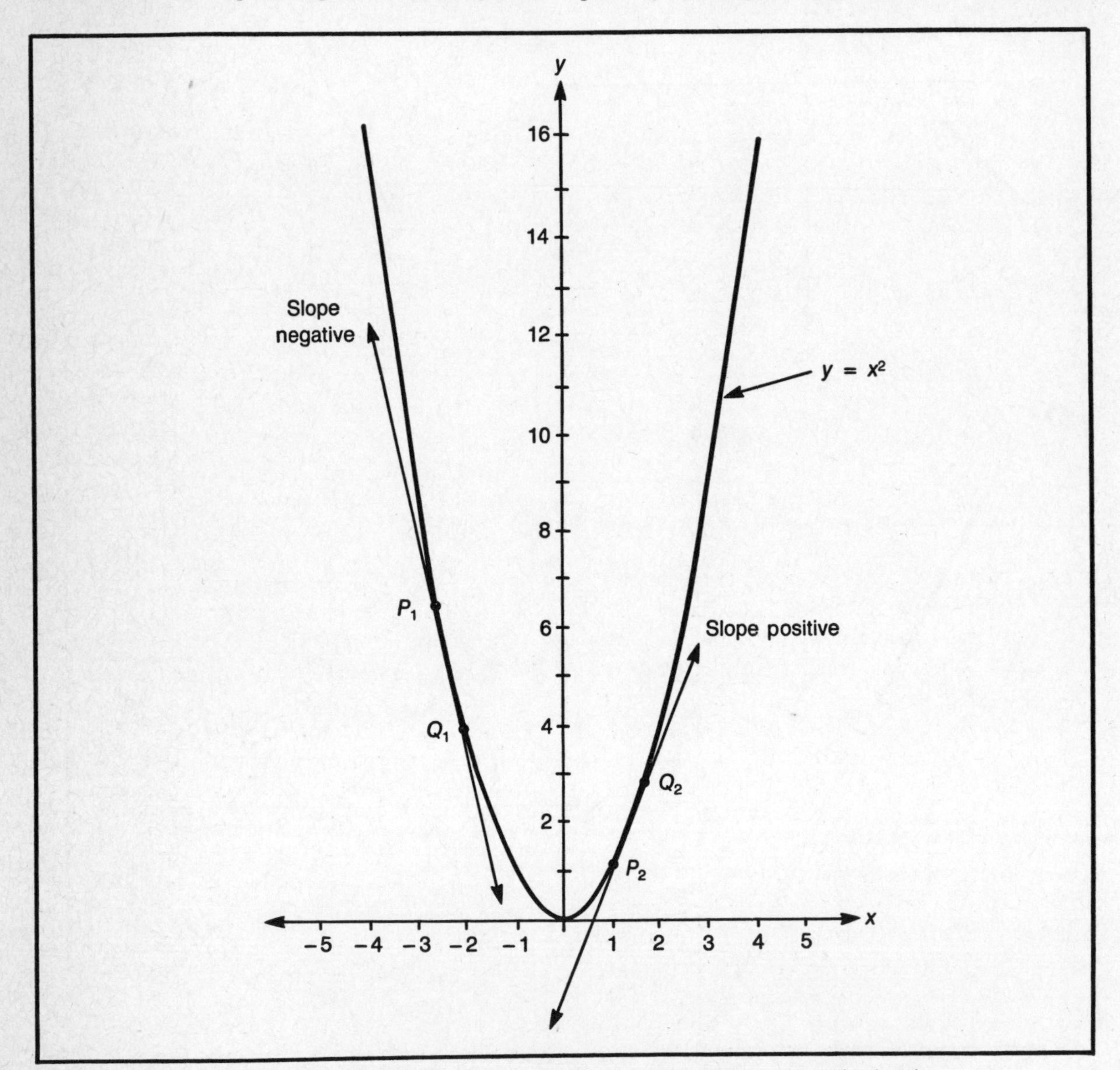

Fig. 3-11. An example of a curve in which the slope is negative in some places and positive in others.

curve at that point. We do this for a certain point (x,y) on a curve by finding the slope of a line containing (x,y) and some other point (x_1,y_1) near it, also on the curve, and moving (x_1,y_1) closer and closer to (x,y). As this is done, the slope of the line through both points approaches the slope of the line through (x,y) tangent to the curve. This can be done for any curve that denotes a continuous—that is unbroken—function in the vicinity of the point (x,y). The slope of a line tangent to a curve at a point (x,y) on the curve is known as the *derivative* of the function at that point. Isaac Newton was the first to work out a generalized method for finding derivatives. He called his technique *calculus*. We find that the derivative, or slope, of the curve $y = x^2$ is equal to twice the value of x at any given point (x,x^2). The tangent line has a negative slope for negative values of x, a positive slope for positive values of x, and zero slope (horizontal) when $x = 0$.

For a function $y = x^n$, we find that the derivative, y', is equal to nx^{n-1}. Thus, for $y = x^3$, the derivative is $3x^2$; for $y = x^4$, $y' = 4x^3$, and so on.

It is not our purpose here to delve into the mechanics of differential calculus, but to demonstrate that there is a way of finding the slope of a tangent line at a point on a curve, using the theory of limits. In all cases the method is the same. We bring two points closer and closer together, finding the limiting value of the slope as the points approach each other. This limiting slope is defined as long as the curve represents a function and the function is continuous, or unbroken, at the point in question. For functions that are not continuous, or for relations that are not functions, there will be points at which the slope is not defined. Two examples are shown in Fig. 3-12. At 3-12A, the function is $y = x^2$ for $x \leq 1$ and $y = x^4$ for $x > 1$. The slope at the point (1,1) is not defined because it is different if we approach the point from the lesser side as opposed to the greater side. The example at 3-12B shows the circle $x^2 + y^2 = 1$. The slope is not defined at the points $(-1,0)$ and $(1,0)$.

Most continuous functions have derivatives that are defined at all points in their domains. The derivative may itself have a derivative; the curve representing the slope of a curve may itself have variable slope. One example is the function $y = x^3$, shown in Fig. 3-13. The curve is shown by the heavy line, the derivative $y' = 3x^2$ by the dotted line, and the second derivative by the intermittent light dotted line. The third derivative is shown by the light solid line, $y''' = 6$. The fourth derivative is the x axis; $y'''' = 0$. Eventually the derivative of any function expressible by exponents only will be the x axis. This is not true of certain functions, however, such as the sine function, which keeps repeating the same familiar waveshape except in different phase positions, for any finite derivative, even the millionth.

Derivatives are used to measure the instantaneous rate of change of a physical quantity, such as speed. If your speed is increasing, such as when you pull away from a stop sign, you are accelerating. Your speed might be increasing at the rate of three miles per hour every second; then your acceleration is 3 mph/sec. Usually acceleration is not constant. The curve at Fig. 3-14 shows a possible acceleration curve for you after you pull away from a stop sign on a highway.

An "instantaneous" quantity is in a certain sense meaningless. How can we talk about something that occurs within a single point of time? Doesn't a point have zero duration, lasting no time at all?

We can resolve this confusion by thinking of a time point as a very short interval of time; in fact, we have the liberty to make a time point as small as we want for convenience. This is a better way to think of it in real terms—but the mathematical reality comes back to haunt us. A true time point, in the mathematical sense, does indeed have zero duration. Yet we are able to tell what is happening in that infinitely minute bit of time. We are, in a way, cheating on reality—physical reality—by using mathematical chicanery in an imaginary universe of absolute perfection.

This brings us back to the idea of Hardyism: the mathematical world is perfect, while the physical one is not. We cannot think for an infinitely small amount of time. We think of the "present" as a certain space of moments; our brains require a certain amount of time to think of what is going

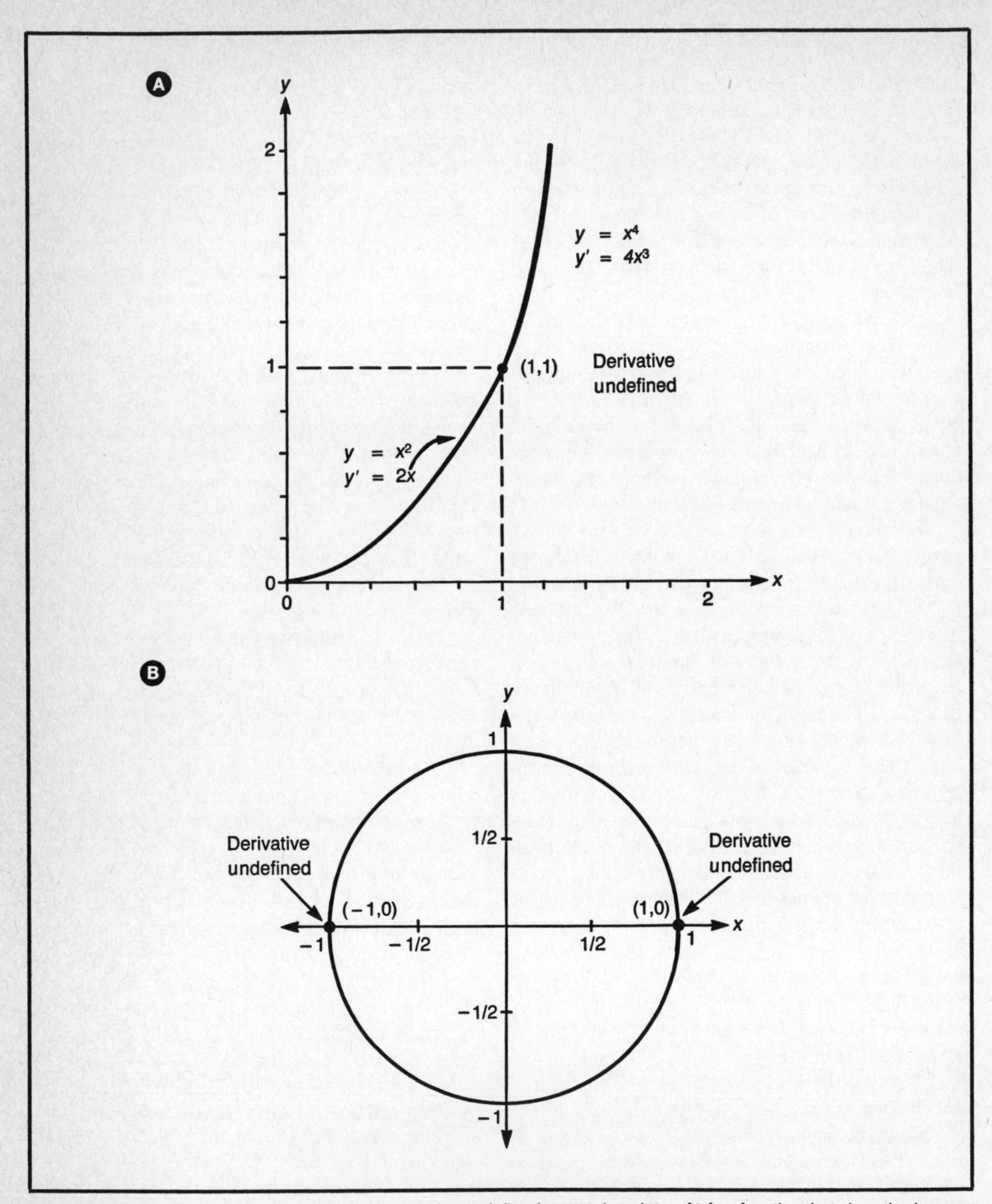

Fig. 3-12. Two examples of curves in which the slope is not defined at certain points. At A, a function that abruptly changes at a certain point; at B, the circle, which is technically not a function but rather a relation.

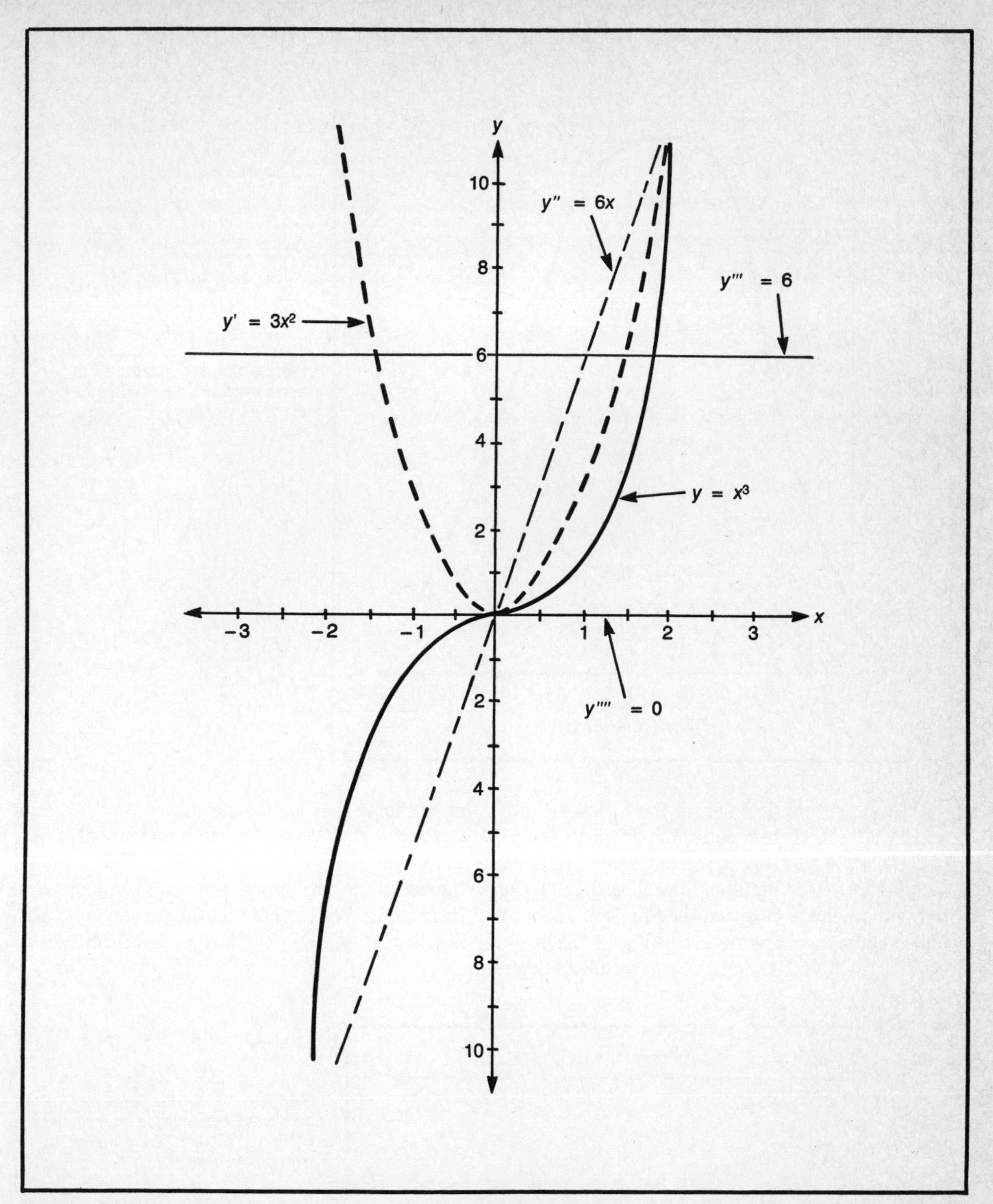

Fig. 3-13. Examples of the first, second, third, and fourth derivatives of a function. In many cases the derivative will eventually become zero.

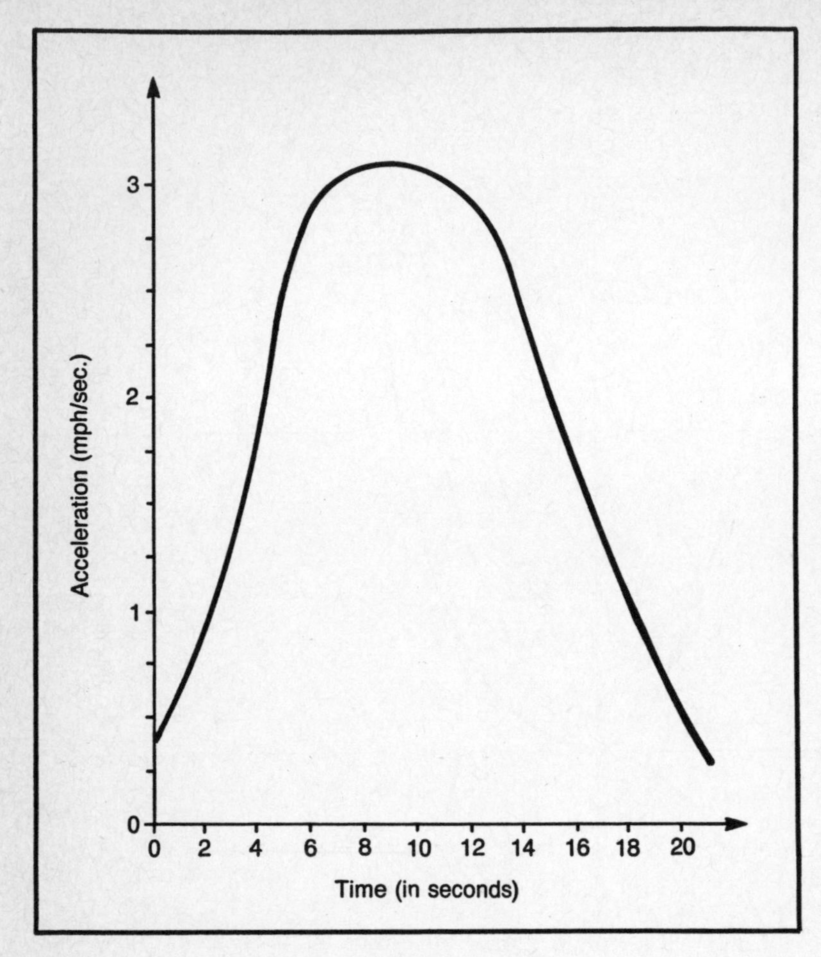

Fig. 3-14. An example of an acceleration curve that might take place as you pull away from a stop sign.

on. So in the physical sense, the "present" is a small, but nonetheless not infinitely small, length of time, with the "future" on one side of the time line and the "past" on the other (Fig. 3-15A). But in the mathematical sense, the "present" is but a point having no duration at all (Fig. 3-15B).

Yet, using mathematics, we are able to determine things that happen during no time. We can figure out what's going on within an interval of time so minute that it doesn't even exist. This is one of the things that makes mathematical phenomena so fascinating. We can commit the paradox of cheating on reality, and get away with it scot-free.

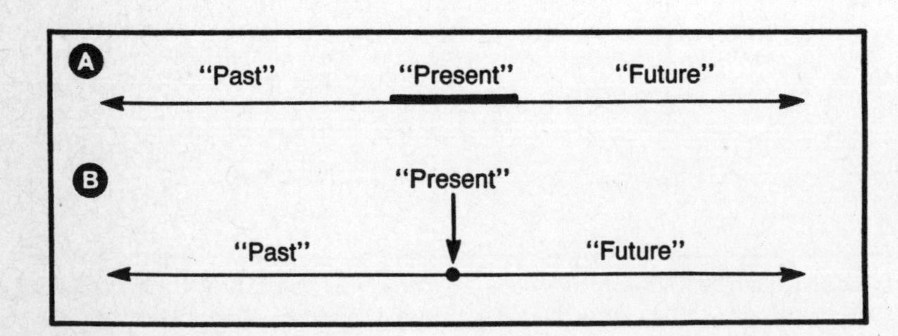

Fig. 3-15. At A, the "present" as perceived in the physical world. At B, the "present" according to mathematical reality.

Chapter 4

Mathematical Universes

OUR PHYSICAL COSMOS IS FULL OF CONSTRAINTS of all kinds. It is so complicated that we will never fully understand it.

Consider, for example, the chair you may be sitting in while you read this. The chair looks simple enough; it has a certain shape, and is solid. No—not solid, but mostly empty space. This is because the chair is really made up of miniscule particles, with vacuum between them, and the particles only occupy a small part of the volume of the chair. What is more, the particles are moving all around, and these particles are themselves comprised of smaller particles, some with positive charge, some with negative charge, and some with no charge. Even these particles are made up of still tinier ones, all moving around in a manner so complicated that it is necessary to describe their positions in terms of statistical probability. How the chair manages to remain a chair, and not turn into a desk or a table or a lamp or a formless blob, is strictly a matter of order resulting from randomness. The probability that the chair will stay a chair is something like 99.99999999999999999999999 percent. There is in fact a chance that the chair might change into something else, but that chance is so small that we can disregard it for practical purposes—but not for mathematical purposes. This is one way in which mathematics differs from the physical sciences: physical universes are imperfect, while mathematical ones are absolutely without flaw.

THE PURE MATHEMATICIAN

In order to understand the world of mathematics—or worlds, since there are infinitely many of them—we must alter our mode of thinking. We can construct a universe based on a set of axioms, and derive consequences from these axioms by means of the basic rules of logic. In a mathematical universe, what is true is always true, and what is false is always false. These are some things that can neither be proven true nor proven false, and these add an element of mystery to some mathematical universes.

Some mathematical universes collapse when a contradiction is found. It is possible that there are some such theory structures today that have built-in contradictions that have not yet been uncovered.

In his book *A Mathematician's Apology*, G. H. Hardy describes the mind of the mathematician in an elegant way. A mathematician is something like an artist. At least this is true for the pure mathematician. In today's world of computerized machines and applied mathematics, we often forget that pure mathematics still exists. The pure mathematician does not require a computer to prove or disprove something; in fact there are things a computer cannot possibly do. The pure mathematician does not think about whether or not his theory, whatever universe he is constructing, can be put to any use. Hardy despaired of applied mathematics to an extreme, but he did point out that the pursuit of a theory can be just downright plain fun. It provides a sort of escape from the imperfect physical world, a respite to a universe where there are unknowns to be discovered, and where, once found, the results stand absolutely.

In a mathematical universe, the chair may remain a chair, or turn into anything you can imagine, as long as the change is consistent logically and does not contain a contradiction.

COLLECTIONS OF THINGS

Aside from pure logic, probably the most fundamental theory of mathematics is the theory of sets. A set is defined as a collection of things, usually numbers, but sometimes other things. A set might have just one element, or several, or infinitely many, or none at all. A set having no elements is called the empty set or null set, and is written $\emptyset$ or $\{\ \}$. Sets having elements are denoted by means of brackets, inside which are listed the elements of the set, such as $\{1,2,3\}$.

Set theory is very much like logic or Boolean algebra. The primary set operations are union and intersection. The union operation is somewhat like the logical OR, and the intersection resembles the logical AND. Figures 4-1A and B show examples of set union (A) and intersection (B). Those elements in the intersection set are those that belong to both sets; the elements of the union set are those that belong to one set or the other, or to both. Sometimes the intersection set is empty; the two sets are then said to be *disjoint*, having no elements in common.

Theorems in set theory follow along the lines of theorems in Boolean algebra, and the proofs are similar. Examples will not be given here. Set theory is dull when it comes to simple proofs, or even complicated proofs, of statements. The interesting things happen in more advanced set theory. Set theory provides the basis for a definition of infinity, and paves the way to a demonstration that are at least two different kinds of infinity. Georg Cantor proved this not so long ago but was ridiculed by his peers at the time. Now his notion of transfinite cardinal numbers—different kinds of infinity—is commonly accepted.

Basically, Cantor's theory is based on the concept of cardinality. The cardinality of a set is simply the number of elements in that set. Hence, the cardinality of the empty set is zero; the cardinality of the set $\{1,2,3,5,12\}$ is five. The cardinality of the whole set of integers $\{\ldots -4,-3,-2,-1,0,1,2,3,4,\ldots\}$ is infinity, in the sense that it is larger than any integer. The cardinality of the set of rational numbers is also infinity. In fact the cardinality of the set of integers is exactly equal to that of the set of rational numbers, and this can be proven rather easily. However, the cardinality of the set of real numbers is not the same as that of the set of rationals. Although both are infinity, one is apparently "larger" than the other. We will have more to say about this in Chapter 6.

Set theory involves two basic concepts for operations: union, denoted by $\cup$, and intersection, denoted by $\cup$. The union of two sets is the set containing all the elements of both sets. The intersection is the set containing only the elements common to both sets. Union and intersection can be represented in graphic form by means of diagrams known as Venn diagrams. Examples of union and intersection of two sets are shown in Fig. 4-1. However we may have three sets, arranged in such a manner that they all come together at a common point, as shown in Fig. 4-2. Their union is of course the whole area of all three sets (shaded). But the intersection of all three sets is just one common

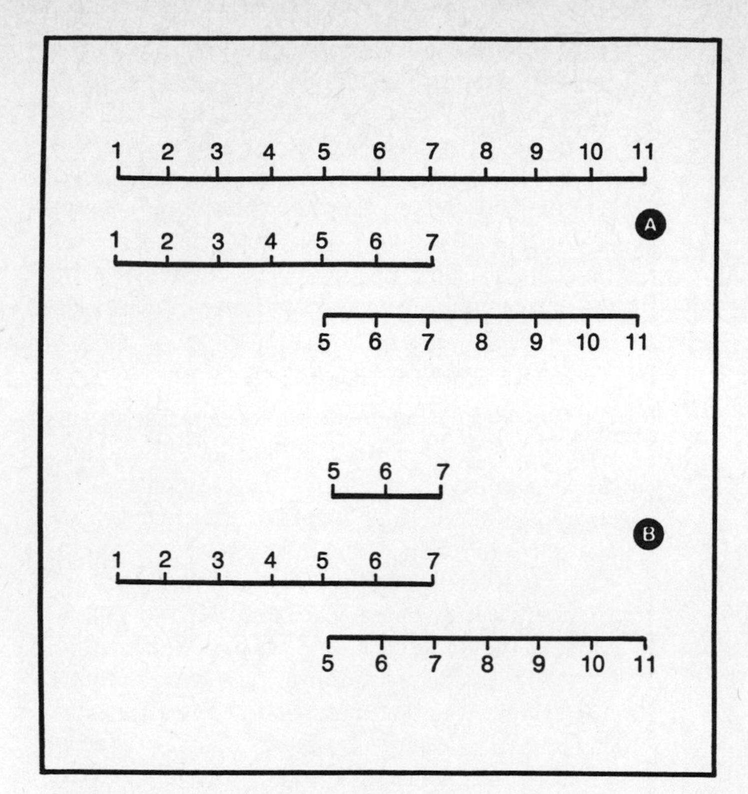

Fig. 4-1. Number-line illustrations of set union (A) and intersection (B).

point, one element. This is true even despite the fact that each of the three sets may contain infinitely many elements.

The interesting thing is that all we need do is move the sets a little inward or outward and, assuming they are "dense" (such as the coordinates in the real-number plane) the intersection must be either the null set, or a set containing infinitely many elements. Figures 4-3A, B, and C show this situation, illustrating the sets as triangles. At A, the triangles are separated so that the sets are disjoint and their intersection has no elements. At B, the points are just touching, so that the intersection contains just that point. At C, the triangles overlap, so the intersection has an infinite number of elements. If we allow the triangles to be moved inward and outward radially in this way, there are only three possibilities for the number of elements in the intersection: zero, one, or infinitely many. It is impossible to have, say, fifteen elements in the intersection, or 15,000, or 15,000,000. It must be either none, one, or infinitely many.

Actually a set need not contain numbers. In the preceding example the sets contain points in planes called "dense"—that is, there is no limit to the fineness into which the plane can be cut up. A set may

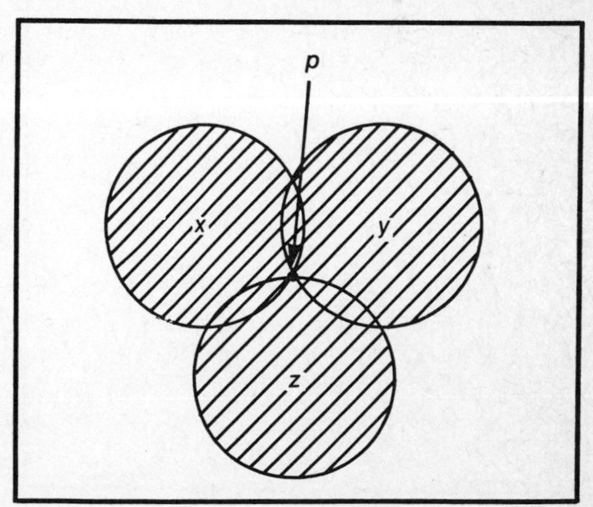

Fig. 4-2. The intersection of three sets *X*, *Y*, and *Z* may be a single point *P*.

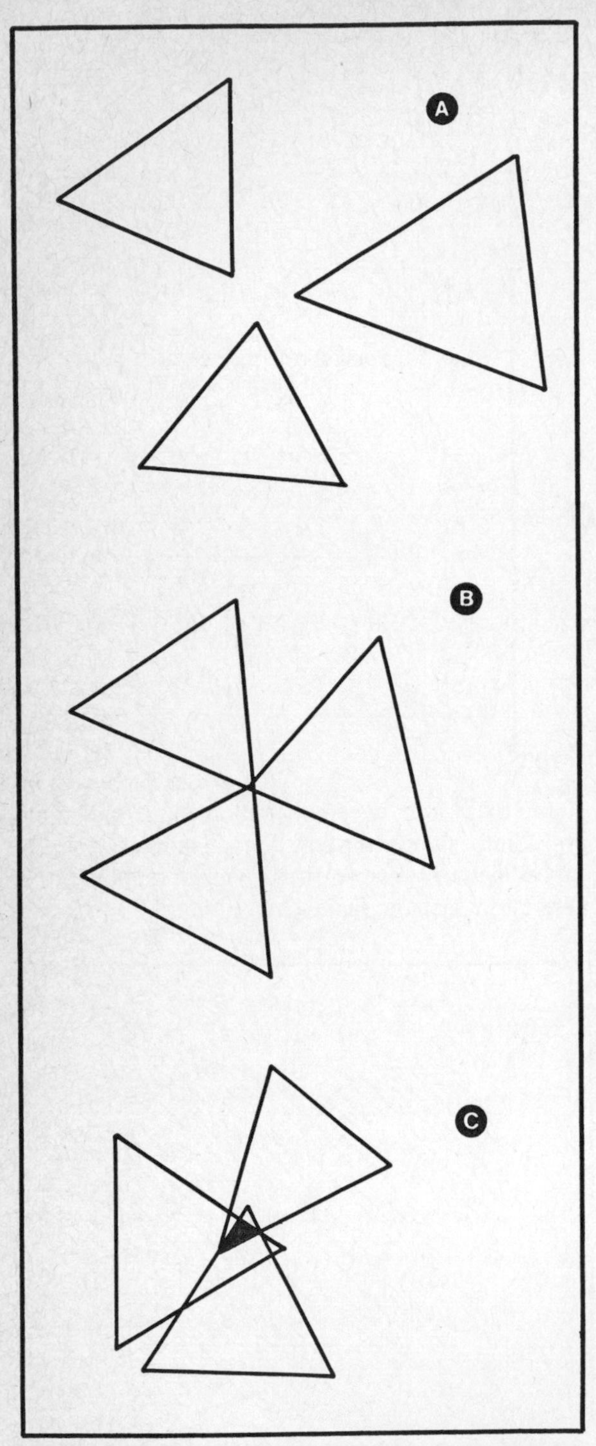

Fig. 4-3. Examples of intersection of three sets being empty (A), containing one element (B), or infinitely many elements (C).

also contain apples, for example. This is one of the imaginary things the mathematician can get away with. You set five apples on a table, and you see five apples. But there is a set containing those apples. What does the set look like? It is nothing but an imaginary thing, invented for the purpose of mathematical inquiry. You might imagine set brackets around a row of apples, but actually the set of five apples has no visible appearance at all.

THE THEORY OF NUMBERS

The idea of "number" is a concept that was invented for the purposes of adding and subtracting, to determine how many things—dollars, for example—might be left before or after a certain occurrence. Numbers were also essential for expressing measured quantities. A decimal system of numbers was invented. The base used was ten, involving the digits 0, 1, 2, 3, 4, 5, 6, 7, 8, and 9.

Perhaps the reason for using a base-ten number system was that man has ten fingers (including thumbs). Counting by fingers is always done by children, and sometimes today by certain accountants and bankers, too! However, base-ten is not necessarily the best system to use. We might have done better if we had begun with a base-eight system, because it is easier to divide quantities in half over and over. This system would involve the digits 0, 1, 2, 3, 4, 5, 6, and 7. We would thus count 1, 2, 3, 4, 5, 6, 7, 10, . . ., 17, 20, . . ., 27, 30, ... A given quantity would appear as at larger number in base-eight than in base-ten, but it would still be the same quantity. However, 10/2 would be equal to 4, not 5; and 4/2 would be equal to 2, as well as 2/2 = 1. We could keep dividing 10, 100, 1000, or any whole round value of 1 followed by zeroes, by 2 until we ultimately got 1. This is not true of the base-ten system.

It is interesting how we have psychological barriers concerning some numbers, such as the year 2000 or breaking 20 seconds in the 50-yard freestyle or running a mile in less than four minutes. If we used base-eight, these "round number" psychological barriers would be different. You might get a thrill when your bank balance exceeds $10,000. But in base-eight this amount would be considerably smaller, to wit:

1	0	0	0	0
4096	512	64	8	1

which gives us a value of $4,096 in base-ten.

Exactly what is a number? The concept generally arises out of the set-theory notion that zero is the set containing the empty set: $0 = \{\phi\}$. Then one is the set containing the empty set and zero: $1 = \{\phi, \{\phi\}\}$. The progression continues, where two is the set containing the empty set and one; three is the set containing the empty set and two; and so on. This is a rather nebulous way of expressing the idea of a number, but from it, all of number theory can be derived. There are other ways as well, but this is the usually accepted one.

If you set five apples on a table, you are looking at apples, not at the number five. Similarly if you write "5" or "V" or some other rendition of the number five, you are looking at the rendition of the number, not at the number itself. A number is an idea, a concept, not a concrete thing. If five apples represented the number five, then five concrete blocks would also, and that would mean that concrete blocks and apples were the same thing. Have you ever tried to eat a concrete block? Or attempted to lay apples as the foundation for a house?

Number theory is one of the few branches of mathematics in which there is still room for discovery of new theorems and ideas, even by high-school and college students. One such idea is the concept of a number that has more than one value. For example, we might have a number with values one, two and three all at once. This may sound like an extremely unpalatable way to express numerical values since it is so vague; but then again, is not the concept of a number itself vague? We cannot see it or touch it or taste it.

From the counting numbers, that is, 1, 2, 3, 4, . . ., we build the rational numbers. These are numbers that can be derived as quotients of the counting numbers, zero, and the negatives of the counting numbers $-1, -2, -3, -4, \ldots$. A rational number is a number of the form a/b, where a and b are integers, that is, counting numbers, zero, and the negatives of the counting numbers. A special qualification is that $b \neq 0$, because division by zero is not defined. Theoretically it is sufficient to say that b may be simply one of the counting numbers. Table 4-1 illustrates a method by which the rational numbers may be constructed.

The rational numbers may at first seem to be all of the numbers that could possibly exist. But they are not. If we take the square root of a rational number, we may end up with another rational number; for example, $\sqrt{25} = 5$. But in some cases there is no rational number that can be found to be exactly equal to the square root of another rational number. The simplest example of this is $\sqrt{2}$. This number is approximately equal to 1.414, but no matter how hard we try, we cannot find any definite repeating cycle to its decimal rendition. All rational numbers have repetition in their decimal

Table 4-1. An Illustration of How the Rational Numbers Are Built up from the Integers. The Top Table Shows the Positive Rationals, and the Bottom Shows the Negative Rationals. Zero Has Not Been Included.

1/1	1/2	1/3	1/4	1/5	1/6	1/7	1/8	1/9	1/10	1/11	1/12	1/13	. . .
2/1	2/2	2/3	2/4	2/5	2/6	2/7	2/8	2/9	2/10	2/11	2/12	2/13	. . .
3/1	3/2	3/3	3/4	3/5	3/6	3/7	3/8	3/9	3/10	3/11	3/12	3/13	. . .
•													
•													
•													
−1/1	−1/2	−1/3	−1/4	−1/5	−1/6	−1/7	−1/8	−1/9	−1/10	−1/11	−1/12	−1/13	. . .
−2/1	−2/2	−2/3	−2/4	−2/5	−2/6	−2/7	−2/8	−2/9	−2/10	−2/11	−2/12	−2/13	. . .
−3/1	−3/2	−3/3	−3/4	−3/5	−3/6	−3/7	−3/8	−3/9	−3/10	−3/11	−3/12	−3/13	. . .
•													
•													
•													

renditions. But some numbers appear to have none. If they do, they haven't been found yet. Computers have been used to calculate $\sqrt{2}$ to thousands of digits and so far no evidence of any repetition been found.

Interestingly enough, although $\sqrt{2}$ is not rational, it can be easily derived in geometric form. This can be done by construction, using nothing more than a compass and a straight edge. First a square is constructed, and then its diagonal drawn. If the sides of the square have a length of 1 unit, then the length of the diagonal is, in theory, exactly equal to $\sqrt{2}$. Not approximately, not even very closely, but exactly. This is shown in Fig. 4-4.

There are other kinds of irrational numbers, too, such as π and e. The number π is the ratio of the circumference of a circle to its diameter. This number has a long history; its existence is fundamental to geometry and even the ancients were aware of it. Originally it was considered to be equal to 3. But recently (comparatively) it has been found to have no exact decimal rendition. An entire book has been filled with the digits of this number, calculated by computer to hundreds of thousands of places. Never has any evidence of repetition been found; evidently π is an irrational number. But it is also apparently not the square root or cube root, or any power root, of a rational number. The number π can be expressed only in terms of an infinite series. This kind of irrational number is called a *transcendental number*. The number e, the natural log base, is equal to about 2.718, and is also a transcendental number. The function $f(x) = e^x$ is unique in that it is its own derivative.

Irrational numbers do exist, even though they cannot be written in decimal form. In fact they are usually simply written only in terms of their symbols, such as is the case with π and e. Any attempt to write the entire decimal rendition for an irrational number is impossible, except in certain peculiar cases where it can be inferred, such as

$$x = 0.1010010001000010000001\ldots$$

In this case the value of any given digit can be predicted, although it is a nonterminating, nonrepeating decimal number. Even so, we can never write it out in full.

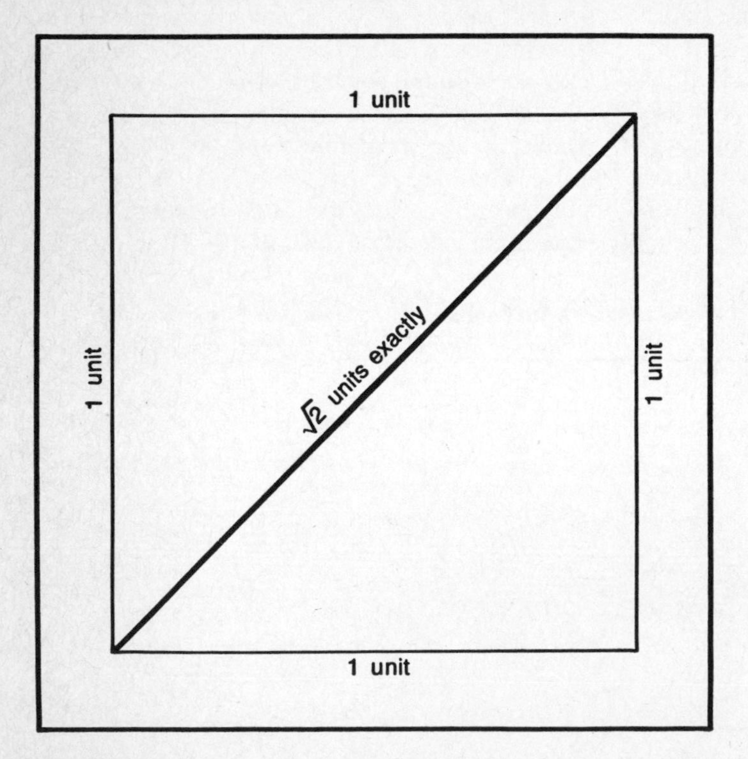

Fig. 4-4. The value of $\sqrt{2}$ can be expressed exactly in geometric terms by means of the diagonal of a square.

The digits of irrational numbers might be considered truly random. The concept of randomness is an extremely difficult thing to resolve, though, as has been pointed out in Chapter 1.

Even though numbers such as π, e, and $\sqrt{2}$ are imperfect in the sense that they cannot be resolved in decimal form, they are perfect in the sense that π represents the ratio of the circumference of a circle to the diameter, and e is the natural log base, and $\sqrt{2}$ represents the diagonal of a square. This is one of the paradoxes of number theory: some numbers can be unresolvable if viewed a certain way, but perfect if looked at another way.

ANALYSIS

Analysis is the study of mathematical relations and functions. It was the specialty of the mathematical purist G. H. Hardy, who looked at all of the mathematics as an art form and decried its being "used" for any particular purpose—at least from his own point of view.

A relation is simply a definable correlation between two numbers, say x and y. We might say, for example, that $x + y = 2$. There is an infinite number of ways that we can find values x and y such that $x + y = 2$; this can be shown in graphical form (Fig. 4-5A). Another example is $x^2 + y^2 = 1$; this is the familiar unit circle (Fig. 4-5B).

Certain types of relations are called functions. A relation is a function if, and only if, it never attains more than one value for any number in its domain. In geometrical terms, this means that if you draw a vertical line in the coordinate system and move it back and forth along the abscissa (the x axis in Figs. 4-5A and B), the vertical line will never intersect the function curve at more than one point. It is easy to see that the relation $x + y = 2$ is a function, but the relation $x^2 + y^2 = 1$ is not.

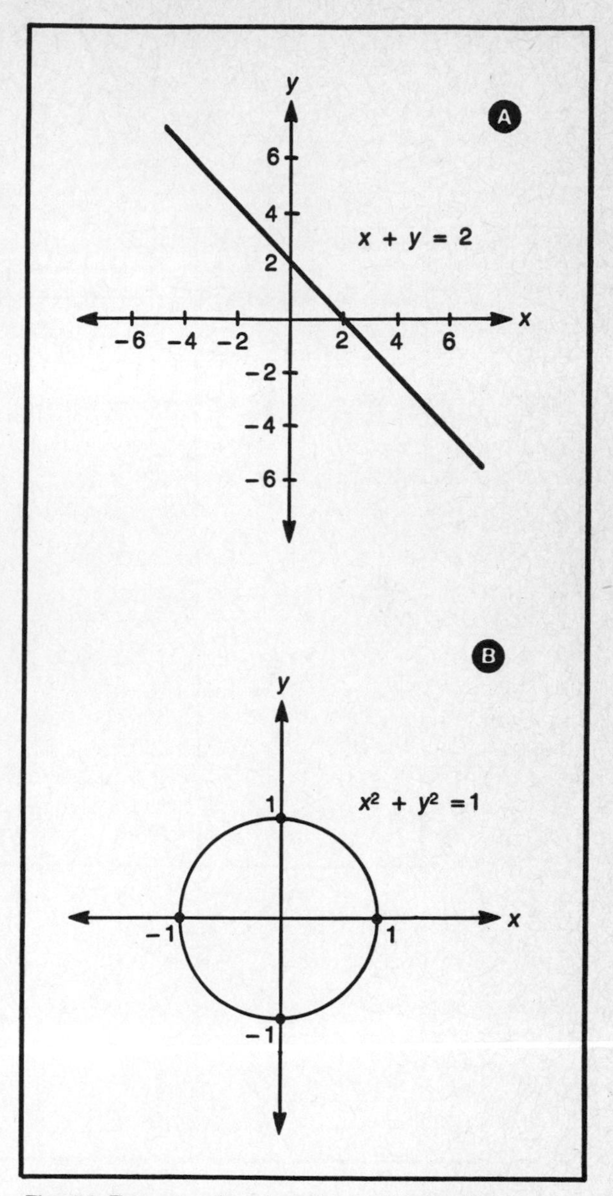

Fig. 4-5. Two examples of relations. At A, the line $x + y = 2$; at B, the circle $x^2 + y^2 = 1$. The line is a function but the circle is not.

Some functions are not functions when different coordinate systems are used. The two most common kinds of coordinate systems are the Cartesian and the polar systems (Figs. 4-6A and B). The Cartesian system uses two axes, perpendicular to each other, the horizontal axis usually called the x axis and the vertical axis the y axis. The polar system uses a radial distance r and an angle θ measured from a horizontal ray pointing toward the right. Variations on these schemes exist but these are the ones most often used.

In the Cartesian system, the circle is a relation but not a function. However, in the polar system, the circle is an extremely simple function, $r = a$, where a is some constant value. In fact, in the po-

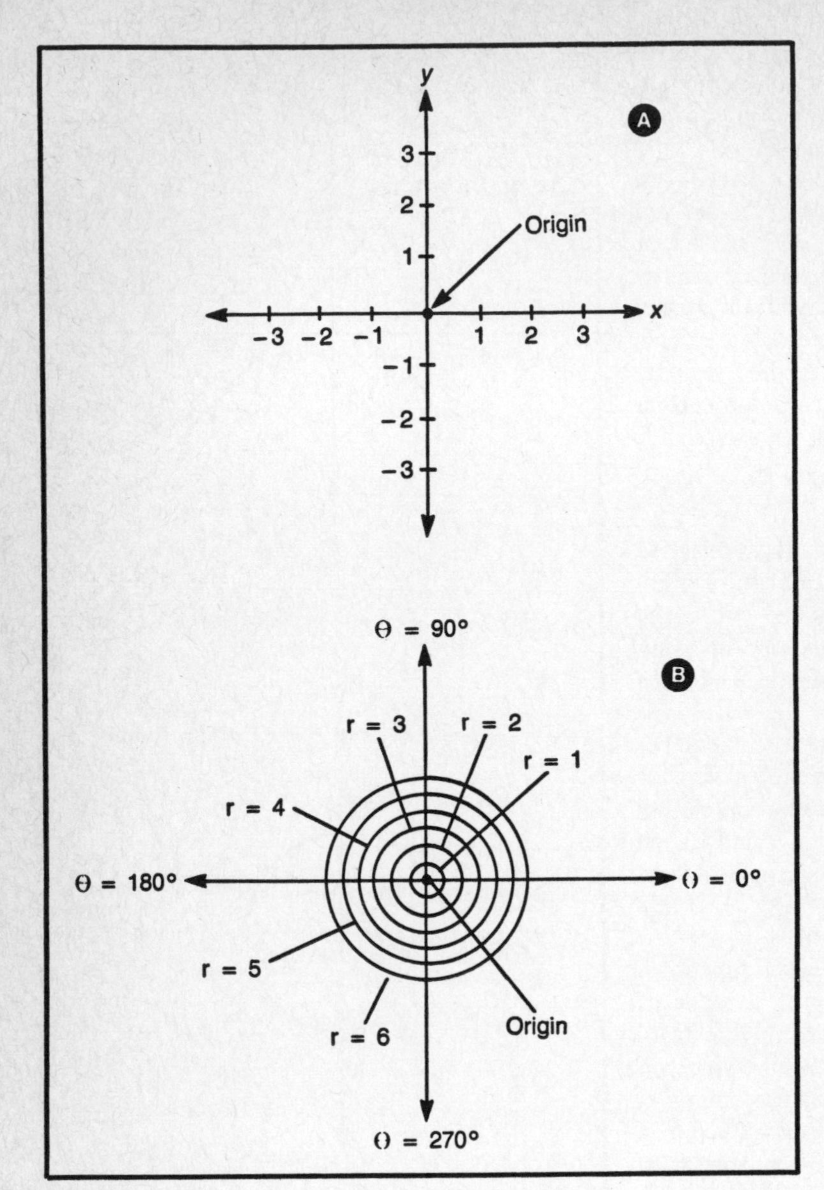

Fig. 4-6. Cartesian (A) and polar (B) coordinate systems.

lar system the circle is the equivalent of a straight line. If we consider r to be the ordinate and θ to be the abscissa, then the circle in polar coordinates is just about the simplest possible function that can exist. Paradoxically, the circle, one of the most frustrating geometrical forms in the Cartesian system, is one of the simplest in the polar system. Also, many straight lines, easy to work with in Cartesian coordinates, are horribly difficult to work with when using the polar system. It all depends on how you look at it.

Analysis is used to examine the nature of functions, and to solve equations involving complex functions. Analysis is a very general topic in mathematics and can be split up into several subcategories, the most significant of which is calculus.

CALCULUS

It was Isaac Newton who first devised a method for determining the instantaneous rate of change for a quantity. His interest was primarily a physical one, involving acceleration. Legend has it that he saw an apple fall from a tree and noticed that it seemed to move faster and faster as it approached the ground. He wondered why this should be, and devised his theory of gravitation from the principle. Gravitation, it turns out, is exactly related to the rate of change in the speed with which an apple falls from a tree.

Calculus can be considered a way of cheating on physical reality. It involves events that take place within infinitely short periods of time. This was discussed in Chapter 3 for differential calculus. But there is an opposite for everything, and the same is true here. The opposite of a derivative is called an *integral*, and the integral is basically the notion of the area under a curve. While velocity is the derivative of absolute position in space, and acceleration is the derivative of velocity, velocity is the integral of acceleration, and position in space is the integral of velocity. All of these are considered with respect to time.

Some curves are easy to integrate. But most involve a certain technique that is best described as an approximation, based on building little rectangles under a curve and then adding up the areas of the rectangles. Figure 4-7 shows the basic principle in qualitative form for some hypothetical curve. The actual area under the curve is approximately the same as the sum of the areas of the little rectangles, constructed in a systematic way so that the centers of the tops of the rectangles intersect the curve. This is in fact the way computers find areas under curves; the rectangles are made very numerous so that the approximation is very close.

Of course, the finer the array of rectangles, the closer the sum of their areas will be to the actual

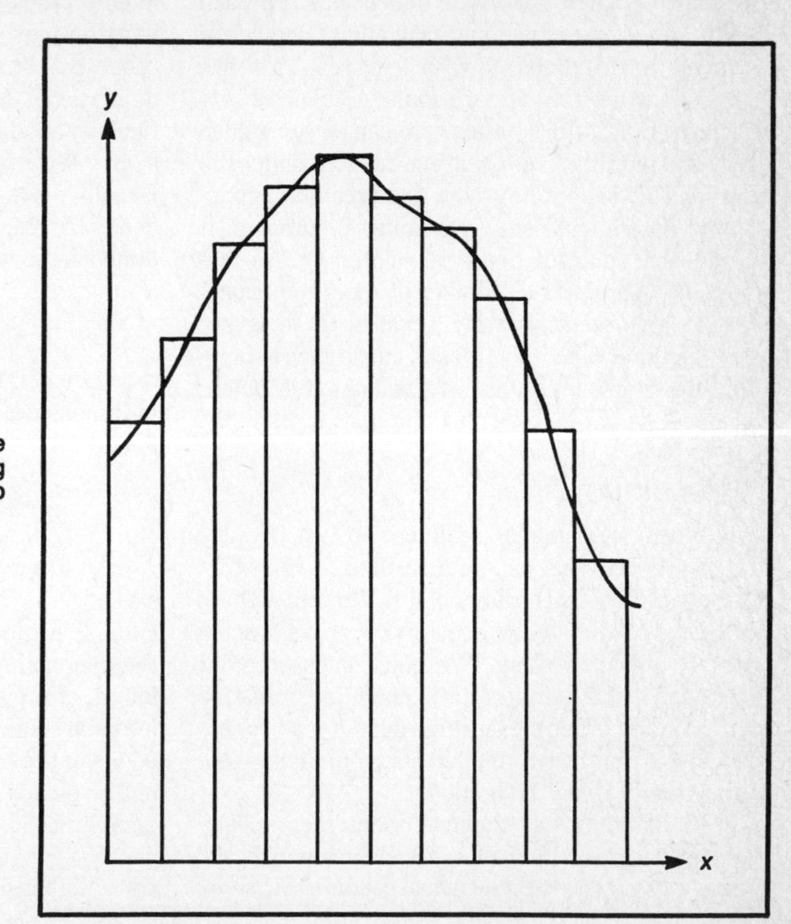

Fig. 4-7. The area under a curve may be approximated by summing the areas of rectangles whose top centers intersect the curve.

area under the curve. But no matter how fine we make the rectangles, the approximation will never be exactly equal to the area under the curve. This might be true in certain special cases, such as when the curve is a straight line or a circular form in which the errors on one side cancel out the errors on the other side. In general, however, the rectangular approximation is never exactly on target. In the world of mathematics, a tiny error, no matter how miniscule, is as good as missing the broad side of a barn.

How, then, do we figure out the exact area under a curve? This is the technique of integral calculus and is similar to the technique used in differential calculus to find the slope of a curve at a given point. We make the rectangles finer and finer,finding the limiting value of the sum of their areas as the rectangles approach infinitely thin proportions (their horizontal dimensions approach zero). In fact the true limit is an infinite number of straight vertical lines, all with zero area. Thus, we might imagine that we are fooling ourselves into thinking that infinity times zero can be some positive real number, representing the area under the curve. This is not altogether an unrealistic supposition, as we shall see in Chapter 6, although it results in a contradiction if taken literally. We cannot add up an infinite number of zeros and expect to get any result, simply because there is not enough time. A computer, asked to do such a thing, would put itself into an infinite loop and, unless stopped, would keep displaying zeroes indefinitely.

DIMENSIONS

When we think of a dimension, we think of some property that can be measured. We say that our space has three dimensions. We might think of time as a dimension also, making time-space a four-dimensional thing. We could even consider such things as temperature, humidity, radiation level, or any other measurable quantity, as dimensions. We can therefore build our environment into a polydimensional hodgepodge.

In mathematics, dimensions can theoretically be constructed without limit to their number. We ordinarily use a two-dimensional coordinate system, such as the Cartesian plane, for graph purposes. Sometimes three-dimensional analysis is done. Computer graphics are especially useful for this purpose, allowing us to view surfaces in perspective. Some programs even let us rotate the object around so that we can see it from different angles. Three-dimensional analysis is much more complicated than two-dimensional analysis; we might find, for example, the orientation of a plane relative to a certain surface in space or the orientation of a line perpendicular to that surface. But it gets more complicated still when we move into worlds of four dimensions and more. Then we are faced not only with more complex sets of equations, but we are deprived of any means of visualizing the situation.

It is not hard to imagine three lines intersecting at a common point, all at right angles to each other. Just take a look at the point where two walls intersect the ceiling of your room. But try, now, and imagine four such lines! You cannot. That is because our space (excluding time) is only three-dimensional. Mathematically, however, it is not difficult to obtain a coordinate system in four dimensions. We might call the axes x_1, x_2, x_3 and x_4. Usually the highest-subscript variable is the dependent variable, in this case x_4, and in a graph in four dimensions, we would thus have

$$x_4 = f(x_1,x_2,x_3)$$

In general, we can have any integral number of dimensions we want. This would in general be denoted by

$$x_n = f(x_1,x_2,x_3, \ldots, x_{n-1})$$

An interesting practice in dimensional analysis concerns the diagonal of a square, cube, hypercube, five-cube, six-cube, and so on. We know that the diagonal of a square is equal to $\sqrt{2}$ times the length of the side of the square. For convenience, let us assume that the sides of the square, or the edges of the cube, hypercube, five-cube, six-cube, and so on are all of length one unit. The square diagonal is shown in Fig. 4-4; the cube diagonal is shown at Fig. 4-8. We cannot even begin to illustrate higher-dimensioned diagonals.

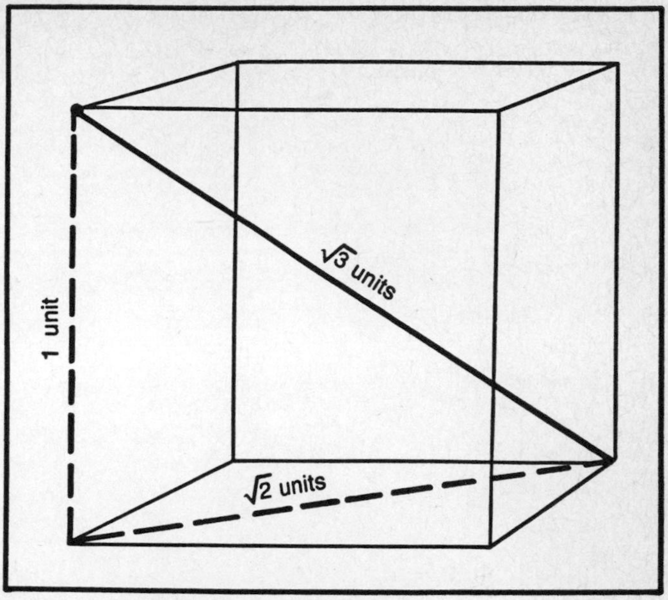

Fig. 4-8. The diagonal of a cube has length $\sqrt{3}$ units. In general, in n dimensions, the diagonal of an n-cube has length $\sqrt{n}$ units.

The length of the diagonal of a cube is greater than the length of the diagonal for a square having edges of the same length. For the unit cube, the diagonal is the hypotenuse of a triangle formed by the diagonal of the base square and the height of the cube, again shown by Fig. 4-8. In this case, if the diagonal is d, then

$$d^2 = \sqrt{2}^2 + 1^2 = 2 + 1 = 3$$

and therefore $d = \sqrt{3}$.

In the case of the four-cube, we find the hypotenuse of a triangle having a base length of $\sqrt{3}$ units and a height of one unit:

$$d^2 = \sqrt{3}^2 + 1^2 = 3 + 1 = 4$$

and consequently $d = \sqrt{4}$ units (which happens to be exactly 2).

It is not difficult to see that in n dimensions, the diagonal will have length $\sqrt{n}$ if the edge of the cube is always one unit in length. The square-root function increases without limit as the abscissa increases without limit. Therefore, as the number of dimensions increases, the diagonal of a unit n-cube also increases without limit. We might imagine then that in infinitely many dimensions the diagonal would be infinitely long. That may or may not be true, depending on the true nature of "infinity." However, we can be sure that in a quadrillion (10^{15}) dimensions the length of the diagonal would be very long indeed. In a googol (10^{100}) dimensions the length of the diagonal of a unit googol-cube would be 10^{10} or 10 billion units! That is hard to imagine, but I suppose no more difficult to conceive of than the idea of a googol-dimensional universe.

Chapter 5

Relativity and the Twin Paradox

ANY MENTION OF EINSTEIN'S THEORY OF RELAtivity brings some people to the brink of an anxiety attack. The first reaction is of some sort of unimaginably complex and esoteric theory, beyond the comprehension of all but the most brilliant scientists. Actually, the theory of relativity is not all that sophisticated. Einstein himself remarked, "God may be sophisticated but he is not malicious," meaning that although the universe is elegant it is not designed with the intention of being too complicated for us to understand. Some of the more recent developments in modern particle physics may lead us to think otherwise, but the special theory of relativity is actually quite simple. The conclusions are esoteric, though, and hard to at first believe.

You have probably heard of the time-aging slowdown that takes place at extremely high speeds. Qualitatively, when you travel very fast, time moves at a slower rate. This is not just an illusion; it can be measured, and it has been shown to occur in scientific experiments. Other effects are quite real, too. Space gets distorted ("squashed") and mass increases as the speed of a moving object approaches the speed of light.

In a vacuum, the speed of light is about 186,282 miles, or 299,792 kilometers, per second. This speed is not dependent on the direction in which the measurement is done, and, oddly enough, it does not depend on whether or not the measuring apparatus is in motion. This observation was regarded as a major paradox around the turn of the century. It was thought that light propagated like sound waves, through the medium of space, and that because of this, its speed would be "constant relative to space." But this did not turn out to be the case.

THE LUMINIFEROUS ETHER

Sound waves could not propagate if there were no air or water or other substance through which it could travel. Acoustic disturbances are a form of *longitudinal wave* in a compressible fluid such as the atmosphere (Fig. 5-1). The molecules of air move back and forth along an axis that lies in the direction of propagation. The molecules move a certain

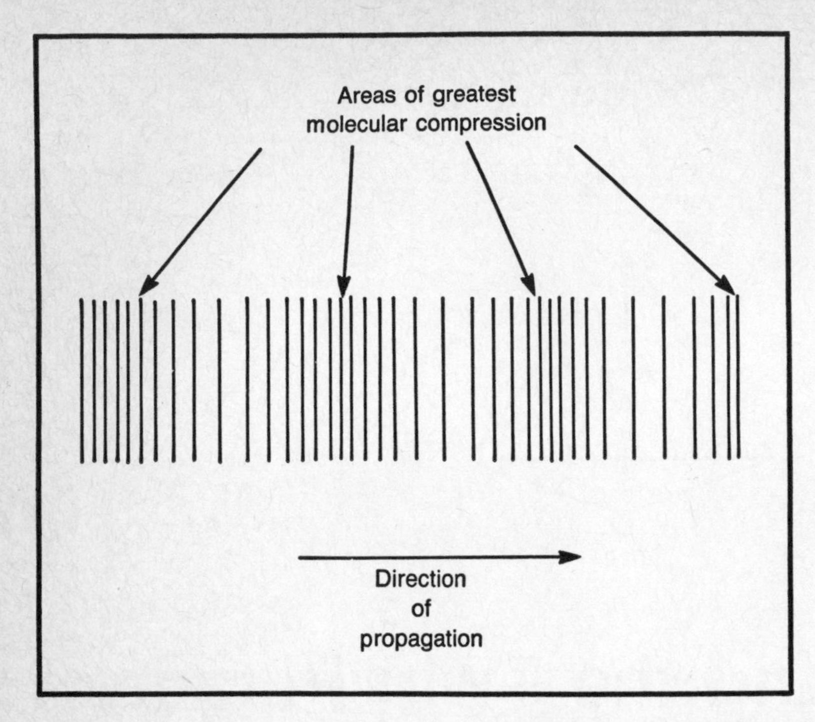

Fig. 5-1. A longitudinal compression wave.

distance back and forth, this distance being greater as the sound intensity becomes greater. Generally the individual particles travel only within a certain distance either way from a center point that remains stationary or moves with the wind. This is true whether the source is moving or not. If the source is stationary with respect to the air in general, the sound waves propagate with equal speed in all directions relative to the source (Fig. 5-2A). If the source is moving, the sound travels away from the source faster in some directions than in others; its movement is fastest with respect to the source in a direction exactly opposite the movement of the source (Fig. 5-2B) and slowest in the direction in which the source is traveling (Fig. 5-2C). In any case the speed of propagation is constant with respect to the air, not necessarily with respect to the point of origin.

Scientists, noticing this property of sound waves and also of waves on the surface of a ripple tank, made the assumption that light behaves in the same manner. This was a completely unfounded assumption, and serves well to illustrate how intuition can subtly lead even the most brilliant minds astray. Believing that light waves travel at a certain constant speed with respect to the "fabric of space," it would follow that we ought to be able to determine an absolute standard of motion for the universe. An object would be standing still in the universe if light waves propagated outward from it, or arrived from space, at equal speeds in all directions.

With this in mind, curiosity took hold and astronomers endeavored to determine this absolute standard for motion. The light from distant stars was captured and measured with precision on the surface of the earth. The speed was checked for different stars in different parts of the heavens, and for individual stars at various times of the day and night and from different points on the globe. Using many different measurements, it seemed that we ought to be able to find out the earth's motion in the universe. It was apparent that this motion would depend on many factors: the spin of the planet itself, its motion around the sun, and the motion of the sun through the heavens (Fig. 5-3). At the turn of the century, the existence of galaxies and clusters of galaxies was not realized, but if it had been, the physicists would have had to include the spin of the galaxy, the movement of the galaxy

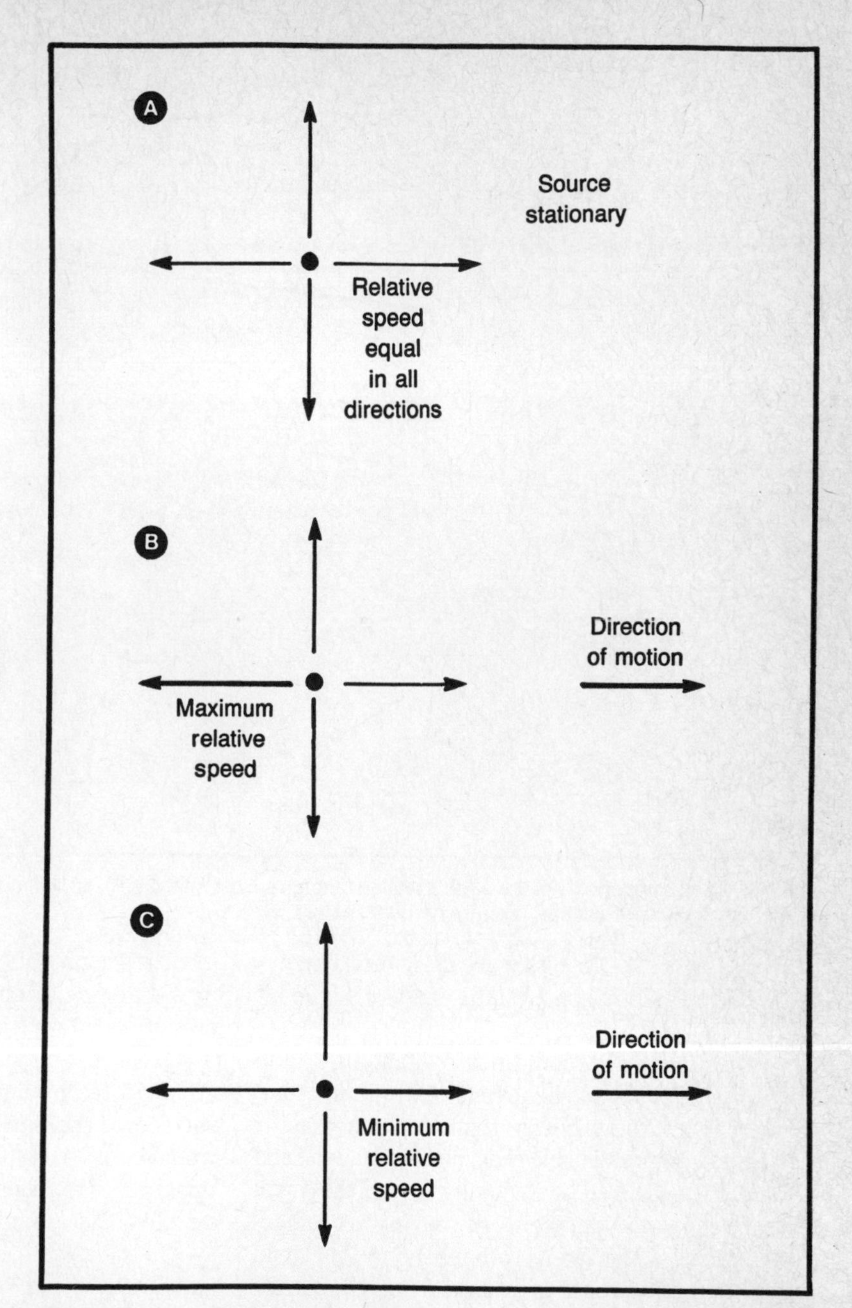

Fig. 5-2. Relative speed of sound propagation with respect to a source that is stationary (A), and moving (B and C).

through its own "local group" of galaxies, and the sojourn of the whole cluster through the greater universe. Even today we are probably ignorant of even larger-scale components of this motion!

One thing seemed certain: because the earth orbits the sun in a path that is roughly circular, our planet cannot be stationary in the universe all the time. This might be the case by coincidence at a few given moments during the year, when all of the components of motion might cancel out, but this would happen only rarely at best and probably not at all.

The results of the experiments were disconcerting. No matter in what direction the speed of light

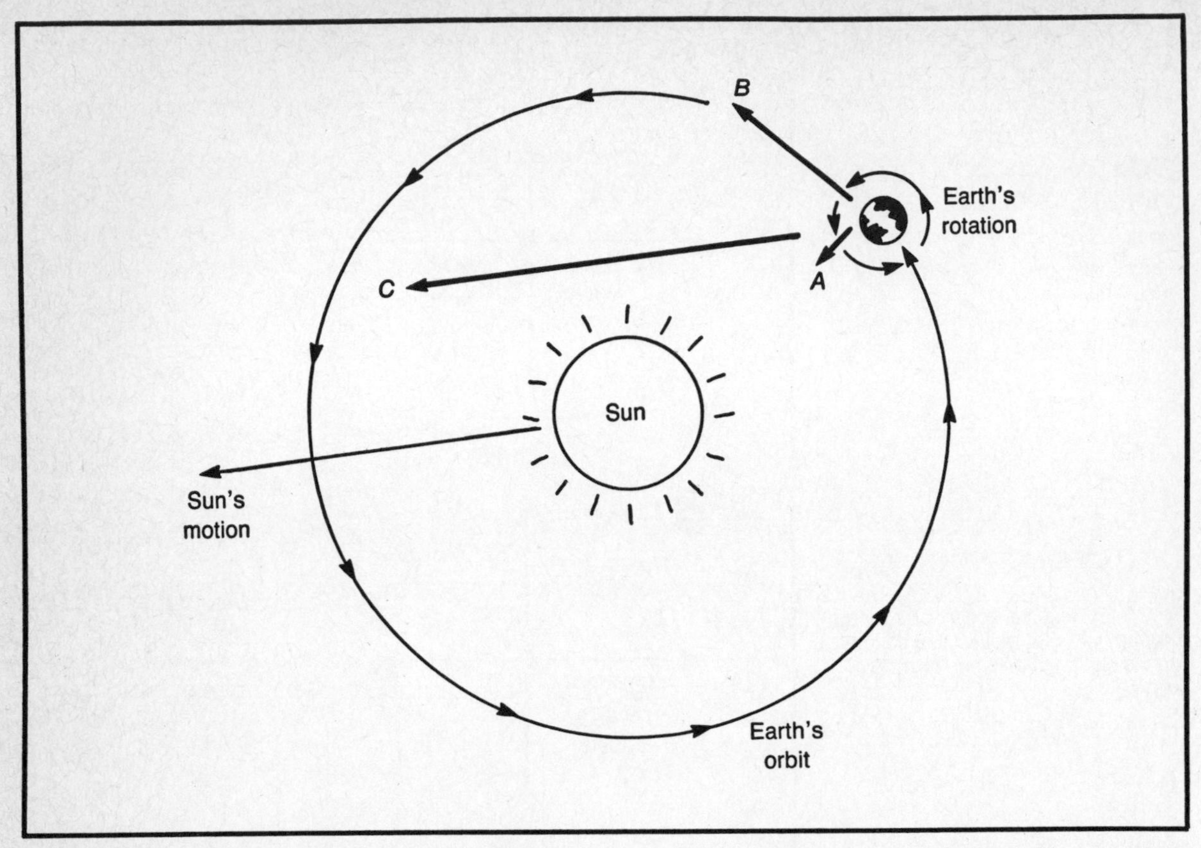

Fig. 5-3. Three components of the earth's motion through space: rotation (A), orbital motion around the sun (B), and motion of the sun and solar system through the heavens (C).

was measured, the results were the same. The motion of the earth in space didn't make a single bit of difference.

Surely the earth could not be standing still in the universe! This was believed in ancient times but modern man knew better than to think that. It seemed incomprehensible that the sun, planets, and distant stars could all be revolving around the earth. Distant stars would have to be moving at tremendous speeds if that were to happen, and it would surely be a coincidence of impossible magnitude for all the stars to be orbiting our planet in such a way as to keep the same pattern in the sky night after night, year after year! How could the results of the experiments be explained?

One possible solution might be that the "fabric of space," the so-called *luminiferous ether*, was stationary with respect to the earth only in the immediate vicinity of our planet. This might be caused by a dragging effect, like that which prevents our own atmosphere from escaping into space because of the earth's motion. Perhaps the atmosphere literally held the luminiferous ether in place near the surface of the earth, making it appear that light would travel at the same speed in all directions. But this theory was soon given up in favor of something simpler: there might be no ether at all.

This was one of the fundamental axioms of Einstein's theory of relativity. We cannot deny the results of experiments; when a theory is contradicted by experiment, that theory has to be changed, or else thrown out altogether. Einstein made the bold assumption that light would have the same speed regardless of the point of view of measurement. The patent-office clerk set out, in his spare time and in the privacy of his little apartment in Switzerland, to determine the consequences of such an axiom. Ultimately the process resulted in the special theory of relativity.

Along with the axiom about the speed of light, Einstein postulated that there could be no "absolute standard for motion" in the universe. Any point of view was just as good as any other insofar as observation of the universe was concerned. This axiom had to be modified later to exclude *accelerating* reference frames, but velocity is of no importance when looking at the cosmos. Neither is physical location per se.

LOCATION AND SIMULTANEITY

The idea of simultaneity—the condition wherein two or more events occur at the same instant of time—seems simple at first. We might say that two events occur simultaneously when, using our best observing methods, they occur at the same instant. Of course true simultaneity can have meaning only to the extent of our ability to measure time; two things that seem to be happening at the same moment according to our body senses might be clearly displaced by using a precision electronic device such as an oscilloscope or atomic clock. The esoteric among us might argue that there really cannot be such a thing as simultaneity, because instants of time in the mathematical sense are points with no duration and must therefore be separated according to the laws of probability. This philosophical argument can lead to a variety of fascinating conclusions, such as the quantization of time, and can even be used to "prove" that time and space do not exist at all. But let us stick to a more physical plane of thought. It is easy to show that simultaneity is a function of position in space.

We can set two clocks so that they show exactly the same time, at least to the best of our ability to determine. With atomic clocks this can be done to within a very small part of a second. Usually we use the National Bureau of Standards for this purpose; you can get the exact time by tuning your shortwave radio receiver to 5, 10, 15, or 20 MHz and listening to the time signals, or by switching your cable TV set to the station that gives the local news and weather. In theory there is no limit to how exactly we can synchronize two clocks so that they agree. But whether or not two clocks will be "synchronized" depends on the point of view from which we look at them.

If you set your watch from a location near the National Bureau of Standards station in Colorado, and then travel far away from that place, you will find that the station doesn't agree with your watch any more. This will be true no matter how accurate your watch. The effect does not occur because of any peculiarity involved with the motion of the traveling process, but because of the propagation of the radio signals through space. Electromagnetic waves travel at the same speed as light—186,282 miles per second—and there is a delay because of this. Even on the surface of our planet, this delay is noticeable. It takes about 1/15 of a second for radio waves to propagate halfway around the world. If you set your watch by station WWV while you are in Colorado, and then go to Australia, you'll sense the difference. Which standard, then, is correct? Is WWV right as you hear it, or your watch right as you read it?

Actually, this is a loaded question. You can use either time standard. Simultaneity, and in fact the idea of a precise time, depends on the place you are. If there are two events, they can be "simultaneous" only if they appear to be simultaneous. In the foregoing example, one event is the ticking of the time-standard station in Colorado, and the other is the watch movement at some place far away from the time station. The two timepieces will seem to agree from some points of view, but not from others.

We can show infinitely many examples of this. The moon is about 1.25 light seconds away from the earth; this means that light, or radio waves, take about 1.25 seconds to traverse this distance through space. There is nothing, at least as far as we know, that travels any faster than electromagnetic fields through the cosmos. Consequently the moon and the earth have time standards, or reference frames, that invariably differ by 1.25 seconds. There is no getting around it. If an event occurs at "the same time" on the moon as an event on the earth, we must qualify our observation by specifying the point of reference. The other planets in the Solar System are light minutes, or hours, from the earth; the nearest star is more than four light *years* from us. Our galaxy is about 100,000 light years in diameter, and our Sun is approximately 40,000 light years from the center of the Milky Way galaxy. When we speak of the whole universe, we speak of incredibly large distances—billions upon billions of light years. The idea of simultaneity for events at widely scattered locations in the universe is completely meaningless.

The situation is totally hopeless if we have four or more events that occur at places that do not lie in a single plane in space. In this kind of complicated situation, it is possible that they cannot be made to appear simultaneous from any point of view. This kind of thing is the rule, not the exception, in our universe.

When we look at the heavens, we see things at various different times in the past. We can actually look at history, although it's not as if we are watching the Crusades or the invasion of France during World War II or the assassination of John F. Kennedy. We can look at stars whose light left them at these times, though, and also at stars whose light left them before the beginnings of recorded history. Some of these stars are relatively close to us, if you care to call trillions of miles "nearby." Some of the most distant galaxies, visible only through large telescopes using special photographic techniques, are so far away that we see them as they were when the earth was scarcely born. Yet we see all of these things, from our point of view, at the same time. If we could look far enough away, we would see the very moment of the creation of the universe. In a sense this has been done using radio telescopes: the remnants of the creation can be detected as faint radio noise coming from all directions in space. It is fitting that this radiation, first observed by Arno Penzias and Robert Wilson in the mid-1960s, was discovered by accident.

TIME DILATION

Motion, as well as physical separation, complicates our perception of time. Motion in fact causes not only a displacement in time, but a change in the apparent rate at which time progresses. The simplest example of this is the so-called Doppler effect, named after the scientist who discovered it. Sound waves provide an everyday example of this phenomenon.

As a train goes by and honks its horn at you, you hear the pitch of the horn go down. This is because the wave train is compressed as the engine comes toward you, and stretched out as it passes and moves away from you. The frequency, or number of vibrations per second, changes. If the horn were to be replaced by a loud series of clicks or beeps generated at 1-second intervals, you would hear them at intervals of less than 1 second as the train came toward you, and at intervals greater than 1 second as it moved away. The same thing happens with radio waves or light beams, although not to a noticeable extent at the speeds achieved by railroad trains. Doppler shift of light beams is a form of time dilation, and at extreme speeds, this dilation can reach large proportions indeed.

Doppler effect is not the only way that time is dilated at extreme speeds, however. There is another form of time dilation, discovered by Einstein and verified by experiments years later. This is the famous relativistic effect. At very high speeds, time slows down, approaching a complete halt as the speed approaches the speed of light.

To illustrate why relativistic time dilation takes place, imagine a spaceship that is 0.186282 miles across, having two mirrors on opposite walls so that a light beam can bounce back and forth between them (Fig. 5-4). This spaceship is of such a diameter that the light beam takes exactly one-millionth of a second to go from one mirror to the other. If we are inside the spaceship, the light beam will appear to take a millionth of a second to go across, regardless of whether the ship is moving or stationary. This is of course a theoretical exercise; in reality the light beam would die out quickly because of imperfections in the mirrors or because of imperfect alignment of the mirrors. But in our minds we can ignore this.

If we observe the ship from outside, the light beam will have to travel farther than 0.186282 miles if the ship is moving. At speeds small compared to the speed of light, this effect will be minimal. How-

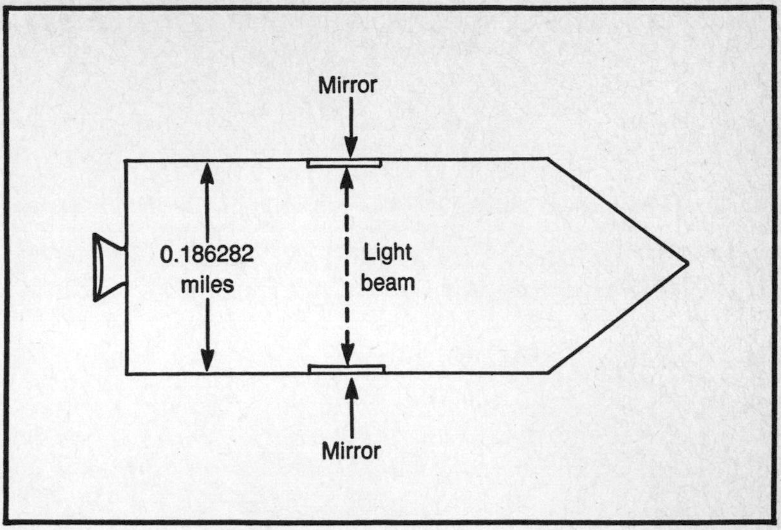

Fig. 5-4. A light-beam clock with an interval of 10^{-6} (a millionth) of a second.

ever, if the ship is moving quite fast compared to the speed of light—that is, an appreciable fraction thereof—the difference will become substantial. This is shown by Figs. 5-5A, B, and C. The light beam, as it bounces back and forth between the mirrors, follows an oblique path through space and does not strike the mirrors at 90-degree angles. Note that from the point of view inside the ship, the situation is exactly the same as it is at rest. Observers inside and outside the ship will *not* see the same thing.

The striking of the light beam against the mirrors might be thought of as a clock, with a "ticking" interval of a millionth of a second. At high speeds, this interval increases significantly as seen from an external point of view. This is not a Doppler shift; it occurs even if the ship moves in a circular path around an external observer, never getting any farther away from, or closer to, that observer.

According to the special theory of relativity, all clocks will behave just like the light-beam clock when relative motion is present. The orbits of electrons around atomic nuclei, the running of any kind of clock, the vibration of a quartz crystal, and even the aging process will be slowed down by a factor f equal to

$$f = \sqrt{1 - v^2/c^2}$$

where v is the relative velocity and c is the speed of light in the same units.

This factor is insignificant if the speed v is a small fraction of the speed of light. But at sizable fractions thereof, the factor gets very significant. The graphs at Fig. 5-6A and B illustrate this factor, which approaches zero as v approaches c. We cannot really say with certainty what occurs when $v = c$, because matter cannot be accelerated to the speed of light. It would take an infinite amount of energy to do this.

DISTORTION OF SPACE AND MASS

A change in the rate of time "flow" is not the only effect of high speeds. The mass of a moving object increases by the factor $1/f$. Therefore, if an object has a mass of m kilograms at rest, the mass m^* for the object in relative motion is

$$m^* = m/f = \frac{m}{\sqrt{1 - v^2/c^2}}$$

This phenomenon is extremely significant, because it means that as v gets very close to c, the mass increases without bound. When mass increases, so does the inertia, and consequently the amount of energy needed to give the object additional speed. The factor $1/f$ is shown graphically in Figs. 5-7A and B.

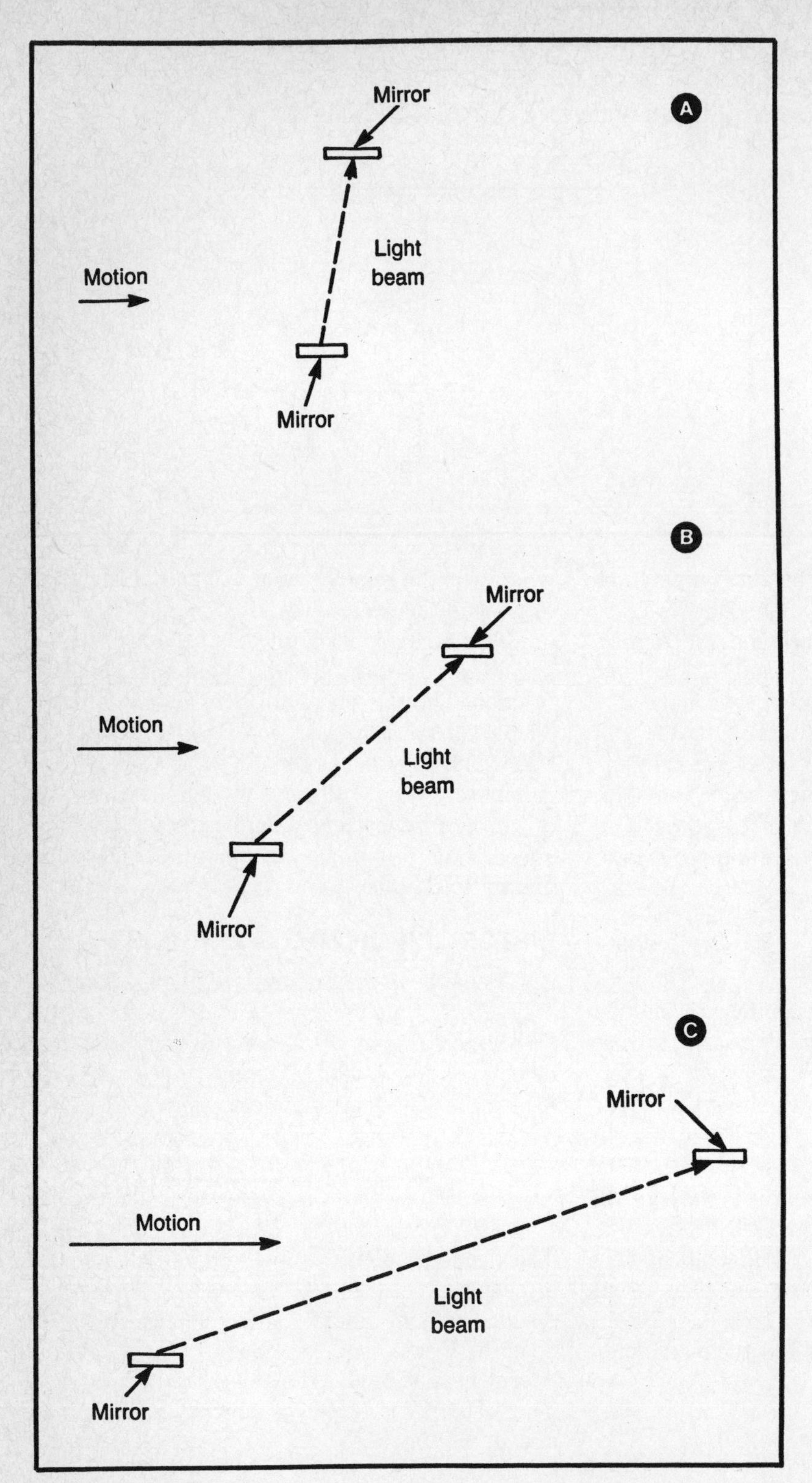

Fig. 5-5. The path of the light beam in the spaceship is lengthened by movement of the vessel. At A, slight effect; at B and C, larger effects caused by greater relative speed.

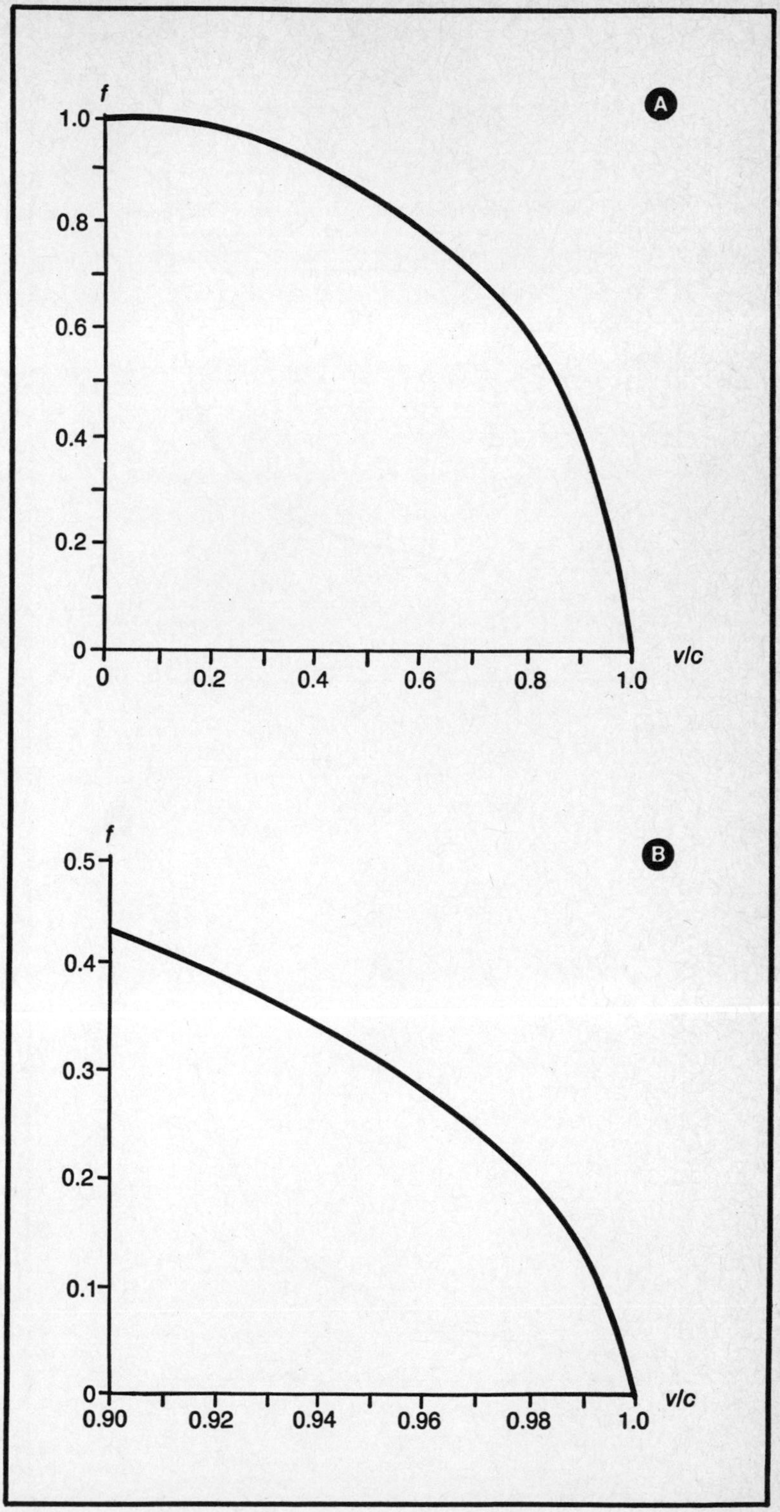

Fig. 5-6. Value of relativistic factor f for various speeds, v/c. At A, over the range $v/c = 0$ to $v/c = 1$; at B, over the range $v/c = 0.90$ to $v/c = 1.0$.

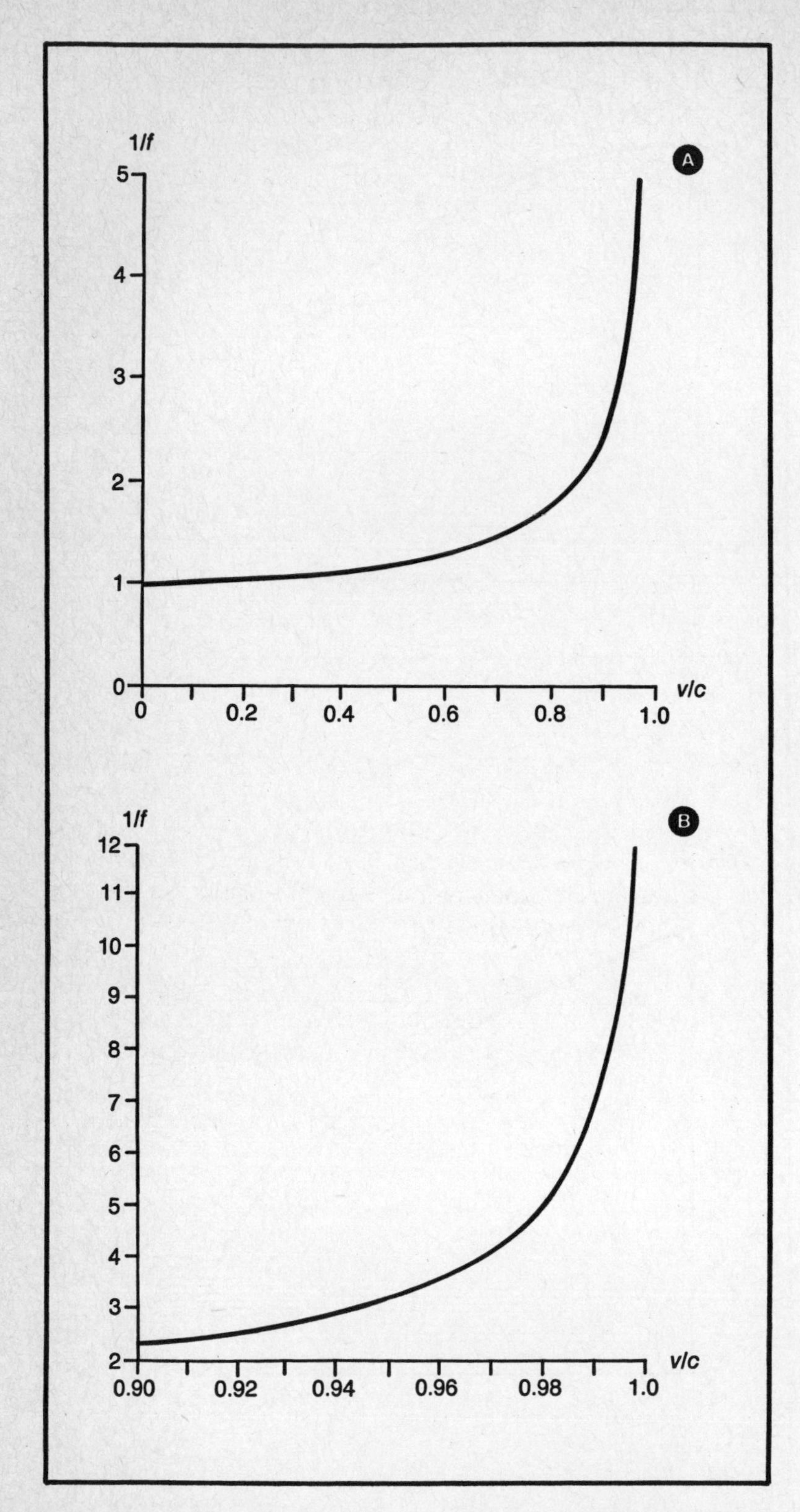

Fig. 5-7. Value of relativistic factor $1/f$ for various speeds, v/c. At A, over the range $v/c = 0$ to $v/c = 1$; at B, over the range $v/c = 0.90$ to $v/c = 1.0$.

Because the mass increases without limit, there is no way that any object can be accelerated to the speed of light. It would take an infinite amount of energy to accomplish this. In theory, there is no limit to how close we can get to the speed of light, however.

Although the effective mass of an object gets larger when that object is in motion, this increase occurs only when the object is seen to be moving with respect to an observer. If we get on a high-speed space vessel and accelerate to high speed, we won't notice the change in our mass. But we will notice that objects external to us, and not moving, will gain mass. This includes meteoroids in interplanetary or interstellar space. It is possible that a pebble-sized meteoroid might mass hundreds of tons, acquiring almost incomprehensible density and penetrating power.

The increase in mass that occurs at high speeds is useful in atomic particle accelerators. Protons, electrons, and neutrons, as well as other atomic nuclei such as alpha particles, become "heavier" when they are moving at extreme speeds. This added momentum gives the particles more force when they are used for atom smashing.

Spatial distortion occurs at high speeds also. When an object is in motion, its dimensions are foreshortened along the axis of motion. This distorts the shape of the object. If the diameter of a spherical object is d units when the object is at rest, its diameter along the axis of motion at a speed v is equal to fd, or

$$d^* = fd = d\sqrt{1 - v^2/c^2}$$

This is shown at Fig. 5-8A, B, and C for a hypothetical spherical object at rest and moving at about 0.9 c, almost the speed of light. The distortion of space becomes complete, in theory, at the speed of light; three dimensions are reduced to two.

We should note that it is academic to say that, when the speed of light is achieved, time stops, mass becomes infinite, and space loses one dimension. It is interesting to imagine this, but because, according to the laws of physics, an object cannot attain the speed of light without becoming energy, there is no practical case in which these effects might be observed. The bizarre conditions of speed-of-light motion can only be approached.

TIME TRAVEL

The dilation of time makes it possible to travel great distances in space without having to worry about not being able to reach a destination within a human lifetime. The nearest star, Proxima Centauri, is over four light years away from our solar system; it would take almost nine years to complete a round trip to this star. But this is nine years as earthbound people would measure it. If we could accelerate to a high enough speed, we could shorten the journey considerably for ourselves. In theory there is no limit to how much we could compress the time. In practice, we are of course limited by the thrust we can get from our engines, and also by the acceleration our bodies could physically withstand for a long period of time.

In his book *Cosmos*, Carl Sagan takes us into an imaginary spaceship capable of accelerating in-

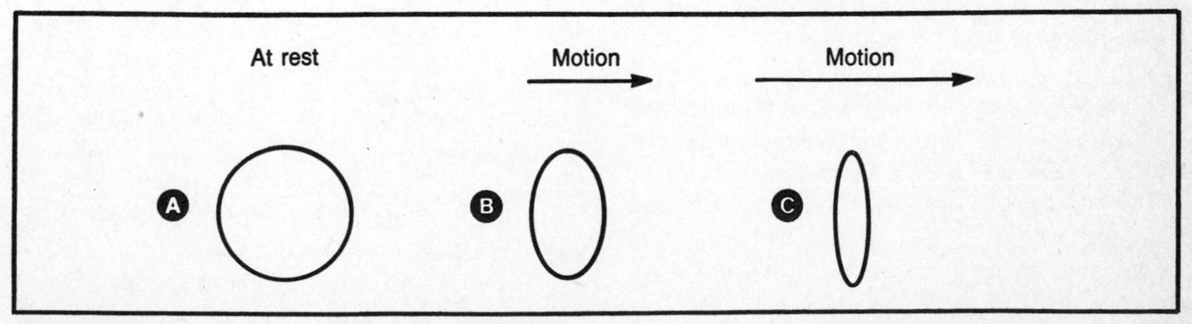

Fig. 5-8. Distortion of a sphere at various speeds. At A, there is no distortion at zero relative speed. At B and C, there is distortion of the axis along which the sphere is moving.

definitely at one gravity, or about 10 meters per second per second. This kind of acceleration—exactly what we are used to as we stand on the surface of our planet—would provide artificial gravity and, over a long period of time, result in near-relativistic speed. It would be possible to travel anywhere in the known universe within the span of a lifetime. All of the distant galaxies and quasars, and all their constituent solar systems and attendant planets, would be within reach. It is not incomprehensible that we might some day have the technology to make a spaceship with this kind of long-range capability. Several designs have been suggested. The most interesting is a device that scoops up the matter in space and uses it to fuel a nuclear-powered thrust device, providing an unlimited fuel supply that doesn't have to be carried in bulky tanks.

The interesting thing about the relativistic effect is that it makes time travel possible, at least into the future. Suppose, for example, that we take a round trip to Proxima Centauri, 4.3 light years from us, and spend just a little time there. If we travel at an average speed of 0.9 *c*, or nine-tenths of the speed of light (167,654 miles per second), we will have a relativistic factor *f* of

$$f = \sqrt{1 - 0.9^2} = \sqrt{1 - 0.81} = \sqrt{0.19} = 0.436$$

For a round trip of 8.6 light years, we would require about 9.56 years to complete this journey, according to those people we left behind on Earth. If we left on January 1, 2000, for example, we would come back sometime in July of the year 2009. But according to our own reckoning, the trip would have taken only 9.56 × 0.436 years, or 4.17 years. Somehow we would have lost the difference, 5.39 years. We would in fact have propelled ourselves into the future by that amount of time.

We might use a more extreme example, and suppose we went to a star 100 light years away at an average speed of 0.99 *c*. At this speed, the round trip would take 101 years according to Earth time; if we left January 1, 2000, we would arrive just after the turn of the year 2101. But the relativistic factor *f* would be

$$f = \sqrt{1 - 0.99^2} = \sqrt{1 - 0.98} = \sqrt{0.02} = 0.141$$

and consequently we would age just 101 × 0.141 years, or 14.2 years. This would be equivalent to traveling almost 87 years into the future! We might return to find that our own children had already died. Or worse, that the world had become such an unfamiliar place that we could not live there anymore.

This sort of thing is not just wild science fantasy, but could actually be done someday. Actually, this effect takes place even aboard spacecraft going to the moon and back, or orbiting the earth; it occurs on airplanes, trains, in cars, and even when you walk across a room (although the effect is negligible in these cases).

In the extreme, we might someday be able to travel so far into the future that the existence of the earth itself might be in doubt upon our return. If we were to go to the farthest parts of our universe, we would return billions of years from now. Scientists tell us that after several billion years, the sun will enlarge to such an extent that it might swallow up the earth; the intense heat would in any case extinguish all life on our planet. Still further into the future, the sun will shrink down to a tiny white dwarf, and the earth will be shrouded in everlasting cold and darkness. Gradually the sun will burn itself out and total entropy will be reached. The planets—those that are not vaporized in the red-giant stage of our sun's evolution—will obediently continue to orbit a dead star the size of the Earth but with the same mass the sun has now.

Ironically the problem with space travel over long distances is the same as the effect that makes such travel possible in the first place. Whenever we go great distances, we are forced to take a one-way trip into the future. There is no way to go back to the same time period as when we leave. Backward time travel has been discussed in many scientific theories, and is the subject of science fiction, but it appears that an actual trip into the past is not possible, at least for us humans. Once the trip has been made into the future, there is no way to get back, ever. What is lost is lost forever.

Some theorists have offered that backward time travel might be done if we could attain speeds faster than the speed of light. This idea stems from the extrapolation of relativistic time dilation. Since time "slows down" and comes to a complete stop at the speed of light, assuming we can reach that speed, this interesting conjecture extrapolates still further and speculates that time would go backward at speeds greater than that of light. Actually this extrapolation is a good example of the logical fallacy so often committed, even by experienced scientists. Simply because some condition is approached, it does not necessarily follow that the condition will be achieved in practice or surpassed should we go beyond the critical point. We know that time slows down and approaches a complete standstill as the speed of an object approaches c; however we cannot conclude from this that time will reverse itself if we go faster than c, or even that time will really come to a stop at c. These are conjectures based on absolutely no proven data. It is the same sort of mistake that has been made concerning division by zero; in fact, the value of $1/f$ does approach 1/0 as f approaches zero (that is, the speed approaches c). But 1/0 is undefined, despite the often-made assumption that it is an "infinite" quantity. We will have more to say about this peculiar twist of mathematics in the next chapter.

Particles have been theorized that travel faster than light and have a time sense that is reversed with respect to ours. These particles are predicted according to the advanced mathematical formulas of particle physics. These strange things are commonly called "tachyons." How we can make use of these particles to travel backward in time is a problem that has not been addressed.

It is possible to prove, via the technique of *reductio ad absurdum*, that traveling backward in time cannot be done. Let us begin with the assumption that we can travel back in time. If this is true, then there is some act that we must commit in order to accomplish the journey. This act might be the throwing of a switch while we sit in a chair in a funny-looking little cubicle in the middle of our uncle's living room. But whatever it consists of, it is some definite act, and by virtue of this fact, the act can be interfered with or prevented. If we in fact commit the act and go back in time a few minutes or hours, we can arrange to prevent the act from having been committed. Therefore we would not have traveled back in time at all. This is a contradiction, and therefore the original assumption—that we can go backward in time—must be false.

There are those who will argue that fate is all predestined anyhow, and we would not be able to change history even if we did go back in time. I can say this much regarding that argument: *I* am not aware that I have ever gone back in time—and if I did I don't remember it—but it doesn't matter to me one way or the other.

THE TWIN PARADOX

We now return to the more real aspect of time travel: relativistic time dilation, which makes it possible to go into the future. You might have a younger brother or sister who would be older than you after you return from a long journey in space. If you have a twin brother or sister, you will not be the same age any more after the trip; the traveler will be younger than the stay-at-home person. The amount of time difference depends on two factors, the average speed of the traveler and the duration of the journey. The longer the trip at a given average speed, the greater the time difference will be at the end; the greater the average speed for a trip of a given duration, the greater the time difference.

Now we get to the difficult-to-resolve paradox. Suppose we have two twin brothers, in spaceships somewhere in the intergalactic void where there is no reference point that can be called "stationary." The special theory of relativity asserts that motion can be ascertained only when there is a reference frame. Suppose these ships are initially hovering close to each other and that there is zero relative motion. The twins—call them Jim and Joe—synchronize their watches so that they read the same date and time. What will happen if Joe speeds off to some distant place, at some high speed, and then returns to Jim, who sits patiently waiting for him without using his engines during that time? According to the special theory of relativity, Jim will see Joe's time flow slow down while Joe is moving. Joe might not have to travel very far away from Jim at all; he might go around Jim in circles for a while, or zig-zag in Jim's vicinity, periodically checking the time. When Joe is finally through, we can conjecture that Joe's clock will be behind Jim's clock by a certain amount that depends on Joe's average speed and the duration of his trip. Joe will be younger than Jim by that amount when the journey is over.

But who says that Joe was moving and Jim was not? If Joe pulls away from Jim and goes a few light years into space and then comes back (Fig. 5-9A), is this any different than Jim going away from Joe (Fig. 5-9B)? Relatively speaking, aren't these two models, one from Jim's point of view and the other from Joe's, identical? Then we should be able to say that Joe will see Jim's time frame as moving slower than his own, and should find that Jim's clock is behind his own when the trip is over. Now we have the paradox. Because both points of view should be equally valid according to the special theory of relativity, it follows that Jim is younger than Joe and Joe is younger than Jim! It is enough to make us want to trash the whole theory of relativity and start over.

We cannot just trash the theory, however. Its conclusions have been proven to be true. An experiment was conducted not long ago in which an airplane was taken aloft having a payload that consisted of an atomic clock, among other things. The time according to this clock was compared with the time according to another, synchronized, atomic clock on the ground. When the plane returned, there was a discrepancy, albeit small, that exactly matched the discrepancy predicted according to the special theory of relativity.

The only way out of this paradox is to accept that there must be some absolute framework to the universe—some standard of motion—after all.

ACCELERATION

The special theory of relativity is concerned with relative motion, but not with acceleration. Einstein postulated that all *non-accelerating* points of reference in the universe were equivalent. How do we know whether or not an object is accelerating? To know this, we need only look at Newtonian physics: any object will remain at rest, or remain in motion in a straight line, unless acted upon by an outside force. The key here is the force. If there is force on an object, its speed changes, and that is the definition of acceleration.

In the example with Jim and Joe, Jim would experience no acceleration, because he did not use his

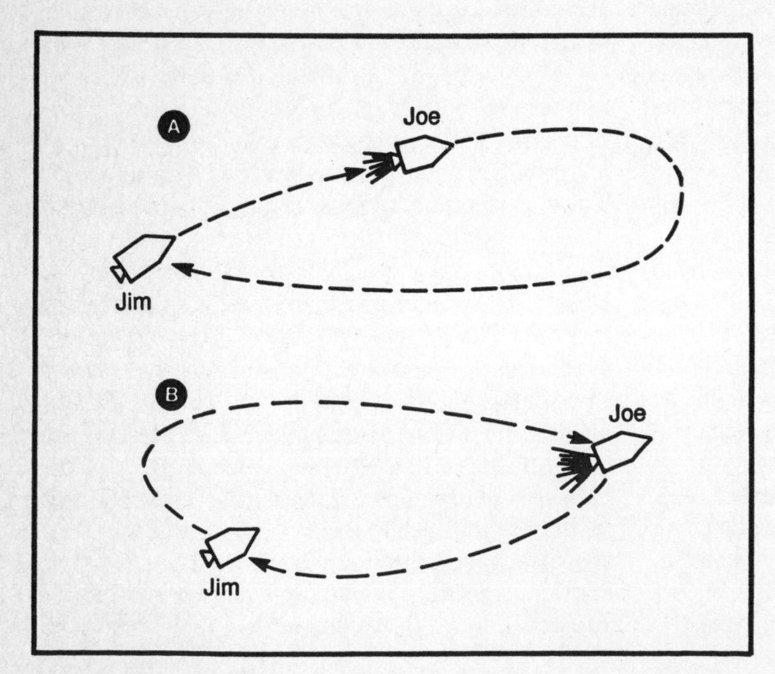

Fig. 5-9. Two ways of looking at a "wandering Joe." At A, from Jim's point of view; at B, from Joe's point of view.

engine. But Joe would experience acceleration. He would notice this acceleration as a force, just like gravity, pulling at him in a direction opposite the direction of the acceleration. In order to get moving, no matter what the path he might take, Joe would have to be accelerating at some time. If he went in a circle around Jim, the acceleration would be constant and inward toward the center of the circle; if he went in a straight line away from Jim and then in a straight line back again, the acceleration would be first away from Jim and then toward him. We can always tell whether or not we are accelerating, because there is always a force that can be measured. Physicists often speak of acceleration in units called *g*'s or gravities, where 1 *g* is the acceleration that produces a force equivalent to the force of gravity on the surface of the earth. This is about 10 meters, or 32 feet, per second per second.

Acceleration is presumed to be the same everywhere in the universe. That is, if we accelerate an object at 10 meters per second per second, the resulting force on an object will be 1 *g*, no matter whether this is done in the solar system or far outside the galaxy. Actually, we cannot be certain of this because we have never checked it in intergalactic space, but we assume at least one thing with reasonable certainty: acceleration, anywhere in space, must be accompanied by force.

This, then, provides a key to the twin paradox. Jim's point of view is *not* the same as Joe's. This is because Joe accelerates during part or all of his journey, whereas Joe does not accelerate during any of that time. The significance of acceleration was realized by Einstein, and led to the expanded general theory of relativity.

GRAVITATION AND NON-EUCLIDEAN SPACE

The force produced by acceleration is just the same, and every bit as real, as the force produced by gravity. If you are accelerated at 10 meters per second per second, you will feel a force of 1 *g*; if you weigh 150 pounds on the surface of the earth, you will also weigh 150 pounds inside a spaceship accelerating at 1 *g*. This is true regardless of whether the acceleration is produced by circular motion, straightforward change in speed, or some combination of change in speed and direction. In fact, if you are inside a completely closed chamber with no way of telling what's going on outside, you cannot know which of these four possibilities—stationary on Earth, changing in straight-line speed, constant circular motion, or some complex motion—is responsible for the force (Fig. 5-10).

Einstein noticed this and proceeded to formulate the axiom that, if we cannot tell by any means, including instrumentation, the difference between acceleration and gravitation, then they are identical, because their effects are identical. This is an axiom because we accept its truth without proof. Should we ever find a contradiction, we would be required to reconsider the truth of the axiom. No contradiction has been found yet.

Acceleration produces a more complicated effect on light and time than a simple relative difference in velocity. Even when an object is moving, light is propagated in straight lines as long as there is no acceleration. This is not true when acceleration occurs; light beams will travel in paths that are curved. The curvature is not significant unless the acceleration is many *g*s; on the surface of the earth it cannot be noticed without precision apparatus. The speed of light does not change; it is always the same, even when there is acceleration. Also, light always takes the shortest path between two points. The strange thing is that this path is not always a straight line. The principles of Euclidean geometry do not hold in space where a strong acceleration, either motion-caused or gravitational, is present.

An acceleration field slows time down because it increases the length of a path traveled by light. This is why Joe's clock will lag behind Jim's in the spaceship example we just examined. Space literally becomes warped, or curved, making the distance traveled by a light beam greater than it would be without the acceleration. We can show this effect by means of a drawing (Fig. 5-11A and B). At A, there is a weak acceleration—comparatively weak—and at B there is a strong acceleration. The light beam "falls" toward the back of the spaceship, traveling a distance greater than the diameter

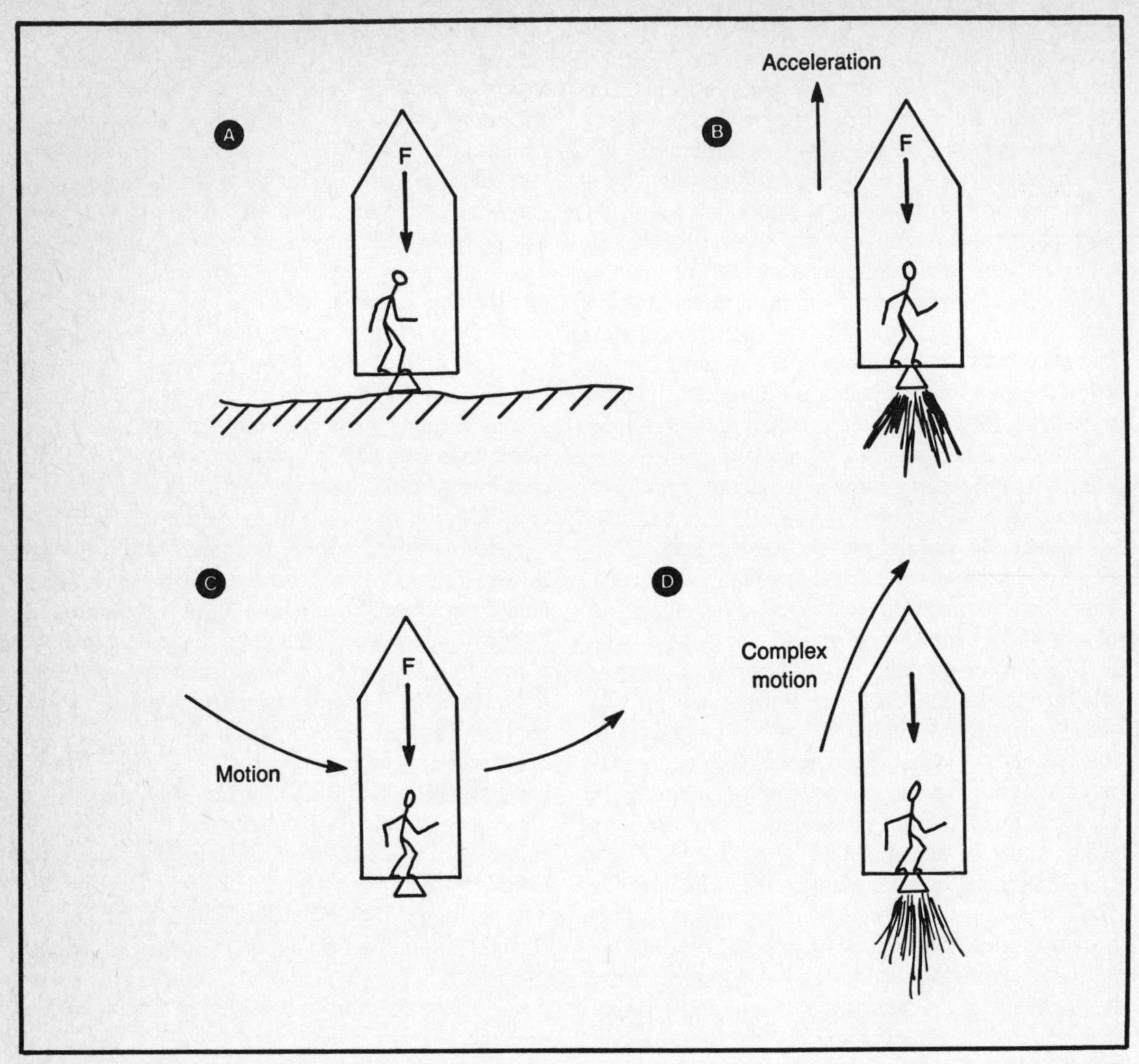

Fig. 5-10. Four ways that a given force F might be felt in a closed chamber. At A, gravity at surface of the earth; at B, force produced by acceleration in a straight line; at C, force produced by circular motion; at D, force caused by a combination of speed change and direction change.

of the ship. If the acceleration is strong enough, the light beam will strike the rear of the ship before it gets to the opposite wall. Despite the fact that it does not look that way in the drawings, the light beam takes the shortest path through the ship under the circumstances: space is actually bent out of shape and there is no such thing as a straight line.

Curvature of space is difficult for most people to imagine because it involves a fourth dimension. Such a mental exercise is made simpler if we liken space to the surface of the earth. The earth's surface is not flat and there is no such thing as a straight-line path along its surface. Yet there is a shortest surface path between, say, New York and San Francisco. The route in this case is a part of a circle. On other curved surfaces the shortest path between two points may not be a circle, but will usually be a curved path.

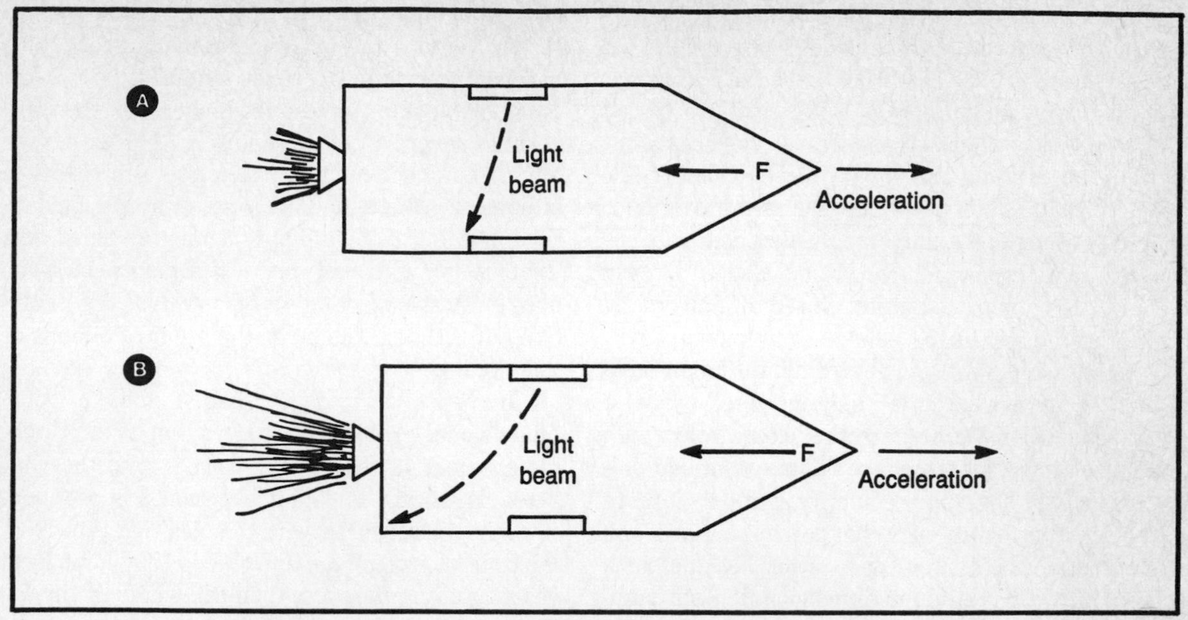

Fig. 5-11. Curvature of light beam produced by comparatively weak acceleration (A) and stronger acceleration (B). Acceleration force is denoted by *F*.

This effect has been verified by experiments in which the light from a distant star is observed as the sun passes very close to the star in the heavens. The position of the star is displaced by the gravitational field of the sun (Fig. 5-12). It is as if the gravitation produces a drag on the photons of light passing near the sun. This isn't quite what happens, but the effect is similar.

BLACK HOLES AND THE CLOSED-UNIVERSE THEORY

If acceleration becomes strong enough, light will not be able to travel at all, except to "fall" in the direction of the force. This would take an enormous, but not infinite, force. If a space vessel could be accelerated fast enough, or if a gravitational field could get strong enough, time would come to a halt,

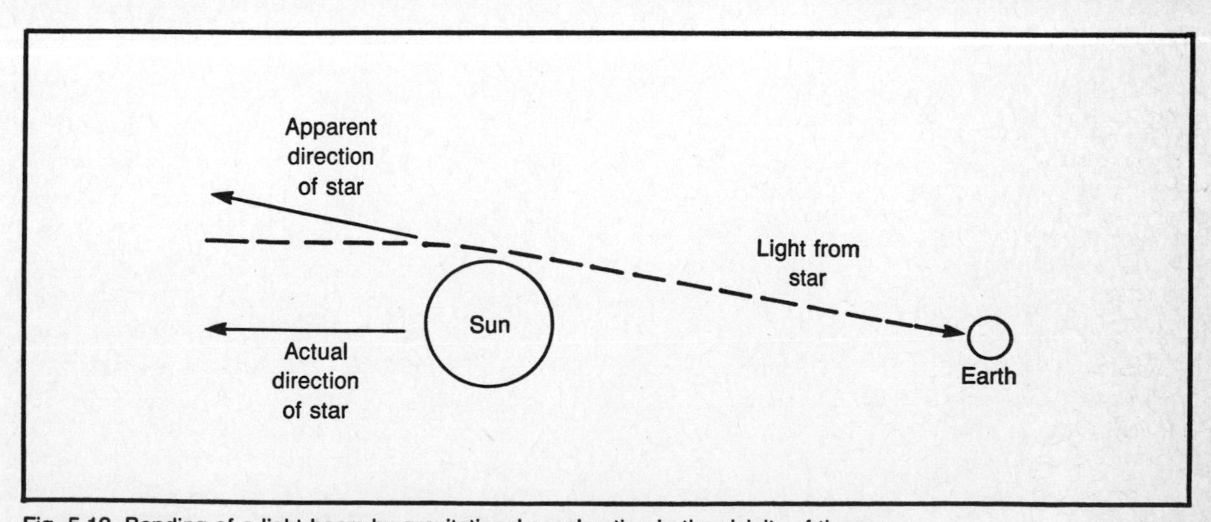

Fig. 5-12. Bending of a light beam by gravitational acceleration in the vicinity of the sun.

space would be infinitely distorted, and all of the familiar laws of physics would be violated or meaningless. This condition, called a space-time *singularity*, can in theory be achieved in collapsing stars having sufficient mass. Some evidence has already been found that such objects, called black holes because light cannot escape their gravitation, actually exist in the universe. In such a strange environment, light and everything else is forever trapped, making a separate, closed-off universe in which time and space behave in unknown ways.

If space curvature is extreme, we might have the condition wherein a "sub-universe" exists, a four-dimensional sphere or other closed object with a three-dimensional surface. This sort of odd universe would have no boundaries, but only a finite volume. Einstein thought that perhaps our own universe might be of this type, rather like the earth itself but with one added dimension. In such a universe, we might travel outward in any direction and, if we went far enough, return to the starting point from the opposite direction. We would, of course, return a long while later, probably at least several billion years later, and find that the local environment had changed dramatically.

As we look out into the depths of space with our most powerful telescopes, is it possible that we are in fact looking around the universe all the way, perhaps several times around? Could it be that we might see our own galaxy as it was some tens of billions of years ago? This is material for speculation only, but the possibility cannot be ruled out. Evidence for a general spherical curvature of space does exist; the exact radius of curvature is speculative but is thought to be on the order of billions of light years.

If space is indeed shaped like a four-dimensional sphere, with us on the three-dimensional surface, every path around this universe is ultimately a huge circle. Philosophers sometimes present us with the idea that time, too, might be a circle; if the universe is 100 billion light years in circumference, then the whole of time is limited to 100 billion years, with no beginning and no end, and all events that ever were, are, or shall be are but points on a time circle, around and around which our existence goes like a captured particle doomed to relive history *ad infinitum*.

Chapter 6

In Pursuit of Infinity

THE CONCEPT OF INFINITY IS NOT NORMALLY REgarded as a number. In our mathematics courses we do not learn much about it, and in fact the term is sometimes introduced without any formal definition at all. Everyone has a notion of "infinity" as some kind of quantity or idea, putting it aside except when the notion happens to be convenient or there is no other way to express a thought. For example, we may speak of the value of a function as a variable "approaches infinity," as if there were some way to sneak up on something unmeasurably and incomprehensibly far off. A common example is to say that as $1/x$ approaches infinity the value of x approaches zero, or vice-versa: as x approaches zero, $1/x$ approaches infinity. In most cases we really should say "increases without limit" rather than "approaches infinity," because division by zero is undefined.

Infinite quantities can be defined, and we can in fact treat such ideas as numbers after a fashion if we are willing to put up with some changes in the way we look at numbers. In this chapter we will attempt to define the idea of infinity and put it along with the real numbers, just as mathematicians have defined the square root of -1 and put it into the realm of numerical values. We can define infinity in various different ways. A common way is to say that infinity is some number larger than any real number; that is, infinity is some x such that $x > y$, where y is any real number. We can add the concept of negative infinity, some w such that $w < z$, where z is any real number. Another way is to define infinity as 1/0, or the tangent of 90 degrees, or the length of the hypotenuse of a triangle with a base angle of 90 degrees, or the distance to the point where parallel lines intersect. Once we have come up with a definition, along with any axioms that we need in order to generate some propositions, we are ready to put infinity into a place along with the numbers. If we eventually arrive at a contradiction, we have to swallow the bitter pill that mathematicians have learned they sometimes must:

we have to watch as our whole beautiful theory comes tumbling down like so much rubbish. But that is the risk of universe building!

MULTI-VALUED NUMBERS

Before we try to define and work with infinity, or some notion of it, we have to prepare ourselves by allowing numbers to take on more than one value. This is a rather shocking idea, perhaps because of its utter simplicity. What is a number, anyway? We express numbers by means of written symbols or words. The number three can be written "3" or "three" or "III." This expresses a concept, but the pure mathematician will tell you that a number is in fact a set containing various elements. (A good text on number theory should be consulted for the rigorous definition of numbers.) In any case a number has one and only one value.

We need not limit ourselves to numbers having just one value, however. We might have numbers with two, three, a hundred, or infinitely many values. For example, a number could have values of both 0 and 1, or 0, ½, and 1, or all the rational values between 0 and 1, or all the real values between 0 and 1. These concepts are illustrated by the number-line drawings of Fig. 6-1. If we include the imaginary numbers, we might allow the values 0, 1, −1, i, and −1 (Fig. 6-2A) or all of the values of z such that $|z| \leq 1$ (Fig. 6-2B).

We will call numbers in general, single-valued or multi-valued, by the term "numerical entities."

You might wonder how it is possible for a number to have more than one value. This trouble, if you have it, might be resolved by pointing out that defining a numerical value is, all by itself, a pretty hard thing to do. The numerical value of three is a figment of the imagination; we can visualize it by thinking of, say, three apples. But we are actually envisioning pieces of fruit, then, and not the numerical value three. We might look at a row of three apples on the same table as a pair of oranges, and think that there are five pieces of fruit, but we will not see the numerical value five. We might just as well think of the values three and two simultaneously, and this is just as close to the entity having numerical values two and three as the other ideas

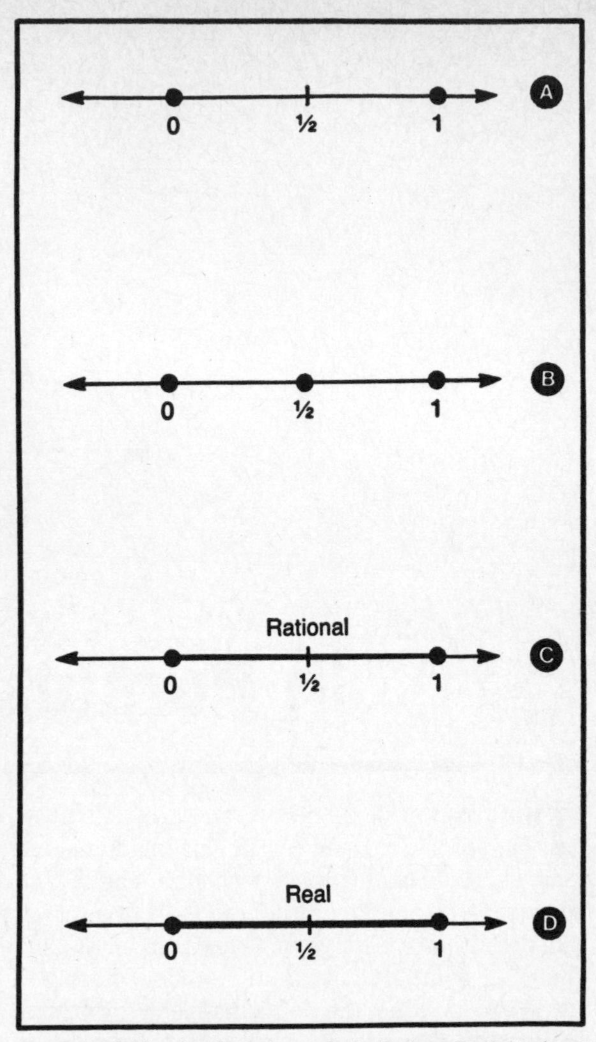

Fig. 6-1. Multi-valued numbers. At A, (0.1); at B, (0,½,1); at C, all rational values between 0 and 1 inclusive; at D, all real values between 0 and 1 inclusive. The rational and real renditions look the same geometrically although they are radically different in theory.

of numerical values were to the actual entities. The concept of a single numerical value is every bit as nebulous as the concept of a multiple one.

The general concept of numerical entities provides a useful way of explaining certain mathematical problems that are puzzling or paradoxical without considering them. The following polynomial is said to have three real-number solutions:

$$(x - 3)(x + 5)(x + 2) = 0$$

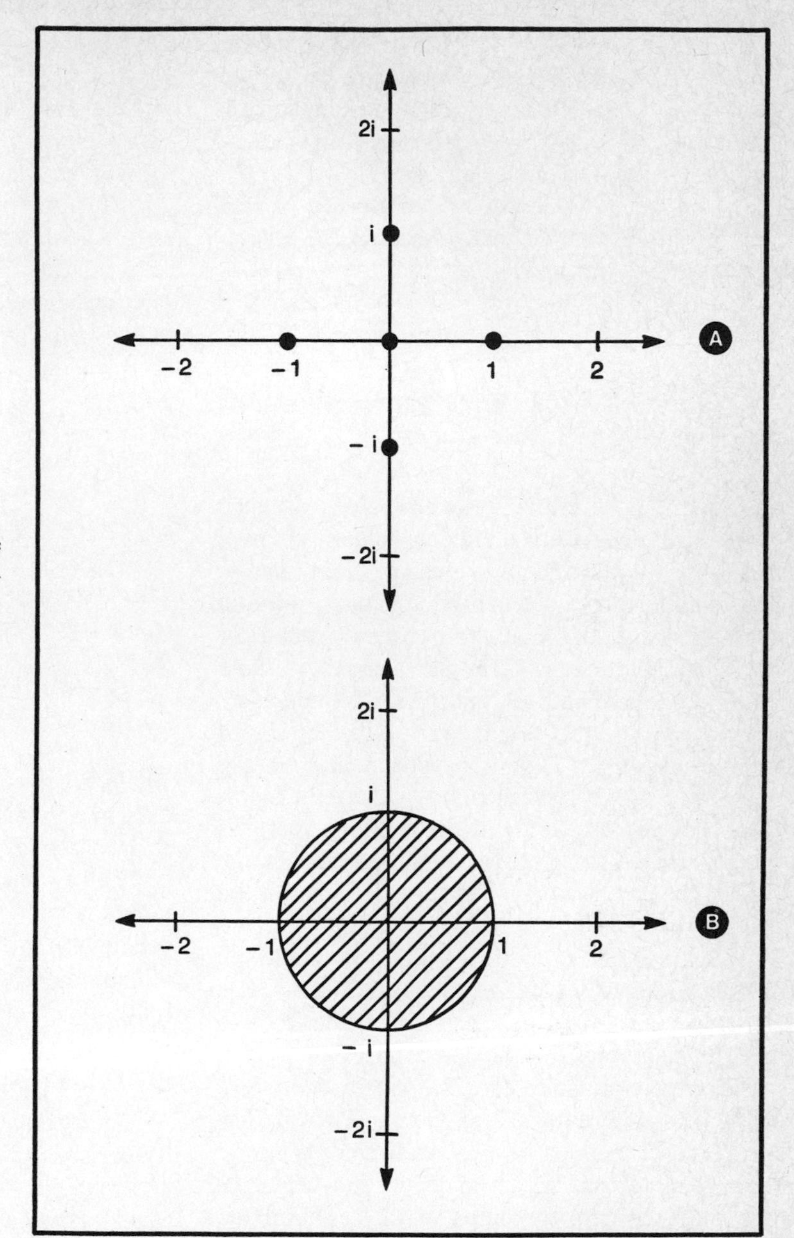

Fig. 6-2. Complex-plane examples of multi-valued numbers. At A, (0, 1, −1, i, −i); at B, all values with an absolute value less than or equal to 1.

You might have seen this in its fully written-out form:

$$x^3 + 4x^2 - 11x - 30 = 0$$

This equation has three real solutions: 3, −5, and −2. This is easy to see by looking at the first (factored-out) form. But we cannot directly answer the question, "What is the solution to this equation?" We can name a set of solutions, namely, the set containing 3, −5, and −2, but there is no single solution. We may say that the solution set, S, is

$$S = \{x: x = 3 \text{ or } x = -5 \text{ or } x = -2\}$$

but we cannot call 3, −5, or −2 "the solution" to this equation.

In order to define a solution for this equation, we must have a number with the three numerical values all at once. This is an academic thing to consider. We can denote the three-valued number by simply writing it in some form such as $(3,-5,-2)$. We do not have to be concerned with order. No one solution is any better than either of the others. Thus, we can just as well say that the solution is $(-2,3,-5)$. The numerical entity corresponds to a *master set*, namely, the solution set, $\{3,-5,-2\}$.

Definition. A numerical entity is a number that takes on one or more values.

From this definition we can see that a numerical entity may have any number of values: one, two, three, twenty, a million, or even infinitely many. The number of values can be countably infinite, such as all rational numbers between 0 and 1, or uncountably infinite, such as all real numbers. Note that a numerical entity is not the same thing as its master set; the entity is simply the values contained in the master set. This may sound like we are speaking of a whitewashed fence without the fence. That the supporting structure (concept of a set) has been removed may seem trivial, but in fact the difference is just as great as it would be with the fence!

The idea of a numerical entity does not imply that all of the values are "equal" to each other. The entity, $(3,-5,-2)$, does not give us the latitude to say, for example, that $3 = -5$, or $-5 = -2$.

For notational purposes, we will write numerical entities using lowercase letters. Thus if $S = \{3,-5,-2\}$, then $s = (3,-5,-2)$. In some cases we will use uppercase letters to denote standard entities, such as R for the entity of all real numbers. To rigorously define the relationship between an entity and its master set, we say the following:

Definition. Given a set A of objects, we define the *entity characterizing* A, generally denoted a, as simply those objects in A. For numbers, a is the combination of numerical values contained by A. The set A is called the *master set* for entity a.

The term *numerical value* is a primitive or undefined term.

We can illustrate this using the general example as follows. If $A = \{a_1,a_2,a_3, \ldots, a_n\}$, where a_i are numbers and $1 \leq i \leq n$, then $a = (a_1,a_2,a_3, \ldots, a_n)$. This applies for entities with finitely many values. If the entity a has infinitely many values, we write the master set first and then replace the set brackets with parentheses. For example, we might have the master set

$$A = \{x: -3 < x \leq 10\}$$

in which case the entity characterizing A is written

$$a = (x: -3 < x \leq 10)$$

This is comprised by real numbers larger than -3 and not greater than (less than or equal to) 10.

Definition. A numerical entity with one value is called *single-valued.*

In the event that $A = \phi$, that is, there are no elements in the set A, the entity corresponding to A does not exist.

The notion of a numerical entity that can take more than one value expands the horizons of number theory, introducing new concepts that will be of help in getting a better idea of the nature of infinity.

EQUALITY BETWEEN ENTITIES

Entity equality is more complicated than equality between ordinary numbers and variables. It is reasonable to say that two numerical entities are equal if they have identical master sets. For example, if we have two sets $A = \{2,5,7,9\}$ and $B = \{6/3, 10/2, 42/6, 27/3\}$, then $A = B$ and therefore their entities are equal; that is, $a = b$. We can also say without any problem that two entities are unequal if their master sets are disjoint. For example, if $A = \{3,6,7\}$ and $B = \{5,8\}$, then the entities a and b are not equal; that is, $a \neq b$. But there is a third condition for numerical entities that does not exist with plain numbers. This is the situation when the two master sets are not the same but are not disjoint. For example, we might have $A = \{1,5,6,8\}$ and $B = \{6,8,10,13\}$. In this case the intersection of the sets is not empty. If C is the intersection, then $C = \{6,8\}$. Can we say of the entities that $a = b$? Not really; they aren't the same. Can we say that $a \neq b$? Yes, but this does not tell the whole story. We have to show that a is something like b, that the two entities share some values. This we call *contingent equality* and we will denote it by saying $a \doteq b$.

Definition. Two entities a and b, with master sets A and B, are *absolutely equal* if and only if $A = B$. In this case we write $a = b$. Two entities a and b are *unequal* or *not equal* if and only if A $B = \emptyset$, that is, if their master sets are disjoint. Then we write $a \neq b$. Two entities a and b are *contingently equal* if and only if $A \cap B \neq \emptyset$. Then we write $a = b$.

Note that two entities are contingently equal if they are absolutely equal. This can be proven easily. Two nondisjoint sets may be identical, and consequently their entities are both contingently and absolutely equal. We can state this as a proposition.

Proposition 6-1. If two entities are absolutely equal then they are contingently equal.

Proof: Given two entities a and b, with master sets A and B, suppose $a = b$. Then $A = B$, and neither A nor B are empty because entities a and b are presumed to exist. Thus, $A \cap B = A = B$, and the intersection is not empty. Consequently by definition $a \doteq b$.

Proposition 6-2. Absolute equality is an equivalence relation.

Proof: Given any entity a with master set A, $A = A$ and therefore $a = a$ by definition. This proves reflexivity. Given two entities a and b with master sets A and B, suppose $a = b$. Then $A = B$ and consequently $B = A$ because set equality is reflexive. By definition, this implies $b = a$, and symmetry is proven. Given entities a, b, and c with master sets A, B, and C, suppose that $A = B$ and $B = C$. Because set equality is transitive, $A = C$ and thus $a = c$. This completes the proof.

Corollary 6-1. If two entities are contingently equal, then it does not follow that they are absolutely equal.

Proof. To show this, we need only provide a counter-example. Given two entities $a = (2,3,4)$ and $b = (4,5,6)$, they are contingently equal because the intersection of their master sets $A = \{2,3,4\}$ and $B = \{4,5,6\}$ is $\{4\}$. However, the two sets A and B are not identical, and hence it is not the case that $a = b$.

Proposition 6-3. Contingent equality is reflexive and symmetric, but is not transitive.

Proof. For any entity a with master set A, $A = A$. Therefore, $A \cap A \neq \emptyset$, since the set A is not empty because a exists by assumption. Because $A = A$, it follows that $a \doteq a$. This proves reflexivity. To prove symmetry, suppose $a \doteq b$. Then the master sets, A and B, are such that $A \cap B \neq \emptyset$. Because set intersection is symmetric, $B \cap A = A \cap B$ and thus $B \cap A \neq \emptyset$. This implies that the characteristic entities are contingently equal: $b \doteq a$. To show that transitivity does not hold, we provide a counterexample. Let $A = \{1,2,3\}$, $B = \{3,4,5\}$, and $C = \{5,6,7\}$. Then their characteristic entities are contingently equal as follows: $a \doteq b$ because $A \cap B = \{3\}$; $b \doteq c$ because $B \cap C = \{5\}$. However, $a \neq c$, because A and C have no elements in common.

These propositions and their proofs may seem rather trivial, but they are of fundamental importance. It is not the purpose of this discussion to give a rigorous, thorough axiomatic demonstration, so we will skip over the innumerable other obvious results, but you can look into them if you are interested.

BASIC OPERATIONS BETWEEN NUMERICAL ENTITIES

We will begin by defining the two most fundamental operations, addition and multiplication.

Definition. Given two numerical entities a and b with master sets A and B, we define $a + b$ as the entity c such that, for each number x in the master set C, x is the sum of some x_a in A and some x_b in B. Also, for every x_a in A and every x_b in B, $x_a + x_b$ is in C. We define the product ab as the entity d such that, for every number x in the master set D, x is the product of some x_a in A and some x_b in B. Also, for every x_a in A and every x_b in B, $x_a x_b$ is in D.

We can show examples. Suppose

$$a = (0,3,6,8) \text{ and}$$
$$b = (-3,1,3)$$

The sum $a + b$ is then

$$a + b = (-3,0,1,3,4,5,6,7,9,11)$$

Each number in the sum's master set is the sum of some number in the master set of a and some number in the master set of b. (We may write the master sets by placing set brackets around the entities, such as $\{a\}$, $\{b\}$ and $\{a + b\}$.) Also, every sum of a number in $\{a\}$ and a number in $\{b\}$ can be found in $\{a + b\}$.

The product ab is

$$ab = (-24,-18,-9,0,3,6,8,9,18,24)$$

You can easily verify this.

We now come to an interesting question: does a given additive inverse exist for an entity a? To answer this, we have to first define what we mean by "additive inverse." With numbers this is quite simple; the additive inverse for a number x is the number y such that $x + y = 0$. That is, $y = -x$. But suppose we have an entity $a = (3,7)$. Can we obtain zero by adding this entity to some other? That is, is there some b such that $a + b = 0$? It is clear that the entity $(-3,-7)$ will not result in zero:

$$(3,7) + (-3,-7) = (0,-4,4) \neq 0$$

It is not difficult to see that there is *no* entity b such that $(3,7) + b = 0$. We can easily find some b such that $(3,7) + b \doteq 0$, however.

We will define additive inverses in a less rigorous manner.

Definition. Given two entities a and b, we say that a and b are *additive inverses* if and only if each x_a in $\{a\}$ possesses an additive inverse in $\{b\}$ and each x_b in $\{b\}$ possesses an additive inverse in $\{a\}$.

When we speak of the additive inverse of a single-valued numerical entity, we are speaking of the familiar "negative" of the number. However, it is *not* in general true that a numerical entity, added to its inverse, will yield exclusively zero. The value zero will always appear in the sum; that is, the sum will always be contingently equal to zero. We can prove the following:

Proposition 6-4. If an entity a is not single-valued, there exists no entity b such that $a + b = 0$.

Proof. Suppose there is such a b. Let the values of a be (x_a), where x_a are real numbers. Let $b = (x_b)$, where x_b are real numbers. Consider two distinct elements of $\{a\}$, x_{a1} and x_{a2}, where $x_{a1} \neq x_{a2}$. Consider also two distinct elements of $\{b\}$, x_{b1} and x_{b2}, where $x_{b1} \neq x_{b2}$. Because $a + b = 0$ (by assertion), it follows that $x_{a1} + x_{b1} = 0$ and also $x_{a1} + x_{b2} = 0$. This is because $x_a + x_b = 0$ for all x_a and x_b. We subtract these equations from each other:

$$\begin{array}{r} x_{a1} + x_{b1} = 0 \\ -x_{a1} - x_{b2} = 0 \\ \hline x_{b1} - x_{b2} = 0 \end{array}$$

This means that $x_{b1} = x_{b2}$. But we assumed these numbers were not equal. This is a contradiction, and therefore our original assumption is false: There is no b such that $a + b = 0$.

Corollary 6-4. If $a + b = 0$ then a and b are both single-valued.

Proof. If one of these entities, say a, is not single-valued, Proposition 6-4 tells us that there is no entity which we can add to a in order to get zero. This contradicts the hypothesis.

We will now look at multiplicative inverses. For single-valued numbers this is a simple concept; y is the multiplicative inverse or reciprocal of x if and only if $y = 1/x$ so that $xy = 1$. The only number that does not have a multiplicative inverse is zero. For entities with more than one numerical value, we run into a problem similar to that encountered with additive inverses, so we have the following definition.

Definition. Given two entities a and b, we say that a and b are *multiplicative inverses* if and only if each x_a in $\{a\}$ possesses a reciprocal in $\{b\}$ and each x_b in $\{b\}$ possesses a reciprocal in $\{a\}$.

When we speak of the reciprocal or multiplicative inverse of a real number x, we mean $1/x$ for $x \neq 0$ and "undefined" for $x = 0$. If an entity is not single-valued, there is no other entity that will exclusively give 1 when the two are multiplied.

Proposition 6-5. If an entity a is not single-valued, then there is no entity b such that $ab = 1$.

Proof. Suppose there is such a b. Let $a = (x_a)$ and $b = (x_b)$ such as in the previous proposition. Consider some x_{a1} in $\{a\}$. Consider x_{b1} and x_{b2} in $\{b\}$, where $x_{b1} \neq x_{b2}$. (None of the x_a or x_b may be zero. This is because if any x_a or x_b is zero, then zero is in the set $\{ab\}$, making ab not absolutely equal to 1.) Because we assume that $ab = 1$, it follows that $x_{a1}x_{b1} = 1$ and $x_{a1}x_{b2} = 1$. Therefore,

$$x_{a1}x_{b1} = x_{a1}x_{b2}$$

Because $x_{a1} \neq 0$, we may divide the above equation by x_{a1}, obtaining

$$\frac{x_{a1}x_{b1}}{x_{a1}} = \frac{x_{a1}x_{b2}}{x_{a1}} = x_{b1} = x_{b2}$$

But we assumed that $x_{b1} \neq x_{b2}$. This is a contradiction. Hence, the original supposition is false, and the proposition is proved.

Corollary 6-5. If $ab = 1$, then both a and b are single-valued.

Proof. This follows immediately from Proposition 6-5.

Proposition 6-6. If zero is in $\{a\}$, then a does not have a multiplicative inverse.

Proof. Zero has no reciprocal in the set of real numbers. Therefore, if we have any entity b consisting of real-number values, it cannot be a multiplicative inverse of a, since no x_b in $\{b\}$ has zero for a reciprocal.

The operation of subtraction follows quite simply from addition, and likewise, division follows from multiplication. We can define subtraction in two ways. We can replace all the plus signs with minus signs in the definition of addition; we can also say that the difference of two entities is the sum of one and the negative of the other. This second definition is stated as follows.

Definition. Given two entities a and b, their difference is defined as the following sum:

$$a - b = a + (-b) = a + -1(b)$$

It is interesting to note that if a is an entity with more than one value, $a - a$ may not necessarily be equal to zero. This is true for numbers but not for entities in general. For example, suppose $a = (1,2,3)$. Then

$$\begin{aligned} a - a &= (1,2,3) - (1,2,3) \\ &= (1,2,3) + -1(1,2,3) \\ &= (1,2,3) + (-1,-2,-3) \end{aligned}$$

We may define division in two ways. We may either evaluate it from the definition for addition, simply substituting the division symbol / for the addition symbol +, or we can say that the quotient of two entities is the product of the first and the reciprocal of the second. These two definitions are equivalent, but this will not be proven here. (You may want to try proving it yourself.) We will define division in the second way, as we defined subtraction in terms of addition.

Definition. Given two entities a and b, in which no element of $\{b\}$ is zero, their quotient is defined as the following product:

$$a/b = a(1/b)$$

where $1/b$ represents the multiplicative inverse of b.

Proposition 6-7. Given two entities a and b, if any x_b in b is zero, then a/b is not defined.

Proof. This is in fact a justification of the definition. We will call an entity "poorly defined" or "improperly defined" if and only if any of its values are undefined. Suppose $a/b = c$. Also, suppose zero is in $\{b\}$. Then for any x_a in $\{a\}$, $x_a/0$ is in $\{c\}$. But $x_a/0$ is undefined for any real number x_a; hence c contains an undefined value. This means that c is poorly defined. For a multiple-valued entity, this is the same as saying that a real-number combination is undefined.

We will soon include values such as $x_a/0$ as defined values, and thus eliminate the gap of poorly defined entities. This gap can be closed, it seems, but the results are quite surprising based on the axioms that seem so intuitively undeniable.

ENTITY OPERATION FACTS

Now that we have defined the four basic operations for numerical entities, we can enumerate various facts about entities. These facts are similar to facts in ordinary arithmetic. We will begin by enumerating facts concerning entity addition and subtraction. These are all easily proved but to give each proof here would be tedious. We will prove just one addition fact and one multiplication fact here; you can prove the rest for yourself if you want (although you'll have to have a high tolerance for boredom!).

First, we must define some abbreviations for entities containing parts of the real-number entity. Let us call the whole set of real numbers $\{R\}$, and the entity corresponding to this set (R). This can be shown as the real-number line (Fig. 6-3A). The set of positive real numbers has an entity corresponding to it, and this we will call $(+R)$. This entity can be illustrated by the ray shown in B. The set of negative real numbers has an entity $(-R)$ as shown in C. Of course, the value 0 is easily shown as a point on the real-number line, as in D. We may also have entities $(0,+R)$ and $(0,-R)$ as shown at E and F. Why do we specifically choose these entities? They represent special parts of the real numbers. We can further subdivide the real numbers into values between -1 and 1, for example, or values less than -1 and greater than 1, but there is, again, a limit to how complicated we want to get!

Addition Facts

The following are examples of addition facts involving real-number entities.

$(+R) + (+R) = (+R)$
$(-R) + (-R) = (-R)$
$(+R) + (-R) = (-R) + (+R) = (R)$
$(+R) + 0 = 0 + (+R) = (+R)$
$(-R) + 0 = 0 + (-R) = (-R)$
$0 + 0 = 0$

Subtraction Facts

The following are examples of subtraction facts involving real-number entities.

$(+R) - (+R) = (R)$
$(-R) - (-R) = (R)$
$(+R) - (-R) = (+R)$
$(-R) - (+R) = (-R)$
$(+R) - 0 = (+R)$
$0 - (+R) = (-R)$
$(-R) - 0 = (-R)$
$0 - (-R) = (+R)$
$0 - 0 = 0$

Proposition 6-8. $(+R) + (+R) = (+R)$.

Proof. We must show two things: first, that a positive real plus a positive real is always a positive real, and second, that any positive real is the sum of two other positive reals. The first is obviously a necessary thing to prove; the second is not so obvious but is necessary in order to be completely rigorous. To prove the first, suppose x and y are positive real numbers. Then $x + y > x$, and

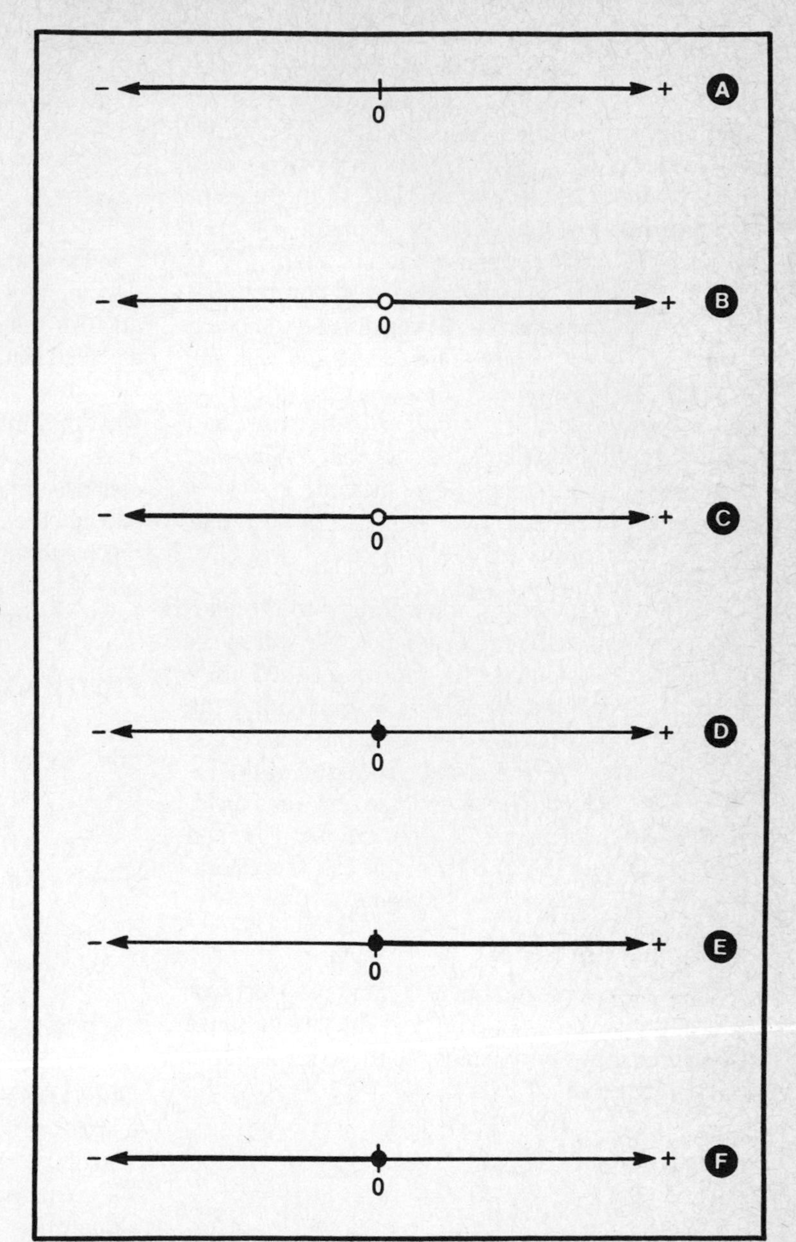

Fig. 6-3. Examples of real entities. At A, all reals; at B, the positive reals; at C, the negative reals; at D, 0; at E, the nonnegative reals; at F, the nonpositive reals.

therefore $x + y$ must also be positive. The sum must also be real, because the sum of two reals is always real. The second fact is a little less trivial to prove. Suppose x is a real number and is positive. Then there exist positive reals v and w such that $v + w = x$. We need find only one example; actually there are infinitely many. Suppose $v = (1/3)x$ and $w = (2/3)x$. We add these:

$$\begin{aligned} v + w &= (1/3)x + (2/3)x \\ &= x\,[(1/3) + (2/3)] \\ &= x\,(1) = x \end{aligned}$$

We can prove that $(-R) + (-R) = (-R)$ very easily; it is an exact mirror-image of this proof.

Proposition 6-9. $(+R) - (+R) = (R)$.

Proof. We must show two things: first, that if x and y are positive real numbers, then $x - y$ may be a positive real, a negative real, or zero, and second, that any real number can be expressed as the difference of two positive reals. To prove the first part, let $x > y$. Then $x - y$ is a positive real number, because $x - y > 0$. Next, suppose $x = y$; then $x - y = 0$. Lastly, suppose $x < y$. Then $x - y < 0$ and therefore is a negative real number. To demonstrate the second assertion, let x be some real number. If $x < 0$, then there exist v and w in the set of positive reals, such that $v - w = x$; let $w = v - x$, for example. If $x = 0$, then there exist v and w in the set of positive reals such that $v - w = x$; the simple example is $v = w$, meaning $v - w = 0$. If $x > 0$, there exist two reals v and w such that $v - w = x$; simply let $v = w + x$.

From this point on, we will refer to the division operation as the ratio operation. We will speak of the expression a/b as the ratio of a to b. This is a more all-encompassing way of expressing the operation for the purpose of chasing the elusive idea of infinity, for we will soon be speaking of the ratio of some real number or entity to zero—and dividing by zero is forbidden. It is our excuse, a method of verbally padding the shock, to call this operation "ratio" rather than "division."

Multiplication Facts

Here are some multiplication and ratio facts for real entities. We will not prove them here, because their proofs are very similar to those for addition and subtraction.

$$(+R)(+R) = (+R)$$
$$(-R)(+R) = (+R)(-R) = (-R)$$
$$(-R)(-R) = (+R)$$
$$(R)0 = 0(R) = 0$$
$$(+R)0 = 0(+R) = 0$$
$$(-R)0 = 0(-R) = 0$$
$$(0)(0) = 0$$

These are just some of the examples that could be given.

Ratio Facts

A few of the examples for the ratio operation follow.

$$(+R)/(+R) = (+R)$$
$$(-R)/(+R) = (+R)/(-R) = (-R)$$
$$(-R)/(-R) = (+R)$$
$$0/(+R) = 0/(-R) = 0$$

The ratio operations with (R) or 0 in the denominator (as the second expression in the operation) are as yet undefined. In order to define these, we need some entity operation axioms. These axioms must hold for *all* real entities, regardless of what they may be. The task of axiom-making is not a light one; if they are too strong, the theory will collapse upon itself, and if they are not strong enough, the theory will have results that don't have much substance. The problem of axiom-making has plagued the mathematician for ages. For our purposes, we will propose only two.

ENTITY AXIOMS

The first axiom involves addition and subtraction. We will call it the Addition Axiom for simplicity.

The Addition Axiom. For all numerical entities a, b, and c:

$$(a + b)/c = a/c + b/c, \text{ and}$$
$$(a - b)/c = a/c - b/c$$

This may be recognized as an expression of the distributive property of the ratio operation over addition and subtraction. Note that we may have $c = 0$ or $c = x$ such that 0 is in $\{x\}$. This is an extension of the axiom as it would apply to real numbers. We are not saying what $a/0$ or $b/0$ or $(a + b)/0$ might actually be; we are only asserting that certain heretofore undefined entities are *absolutely equal.*

The second axiom involves only multiplication and the ratio operation.

The Ratio Axiom. For all numerical entities a, b, and c:

$$\frac{a}{b/c} = a(c/b) = (ac)/b = \frac{c}{b/a}$$

THE ENTITY I

It has long been tempting for students of mathematics, and scientists in general, to think that 1/0 is equal to "infinity." This is based on intuition. For various values of x in the set of positive reals, the value of $1/x$ gets larger and larger as x approaches zero. There is no limit to how large x may be. This is shown geometrically in Fig. 6-4. The nomographs are positive-real-number lines illustrating reciprocals. The reciprocal point, p^*, vanishes off into the wild blue yonder as the base point p approaches zero. Where p^* will end up when p is at zero is anybody's guess, but it doesn't seem altogether out of reason to suppose that p^* is at "in-

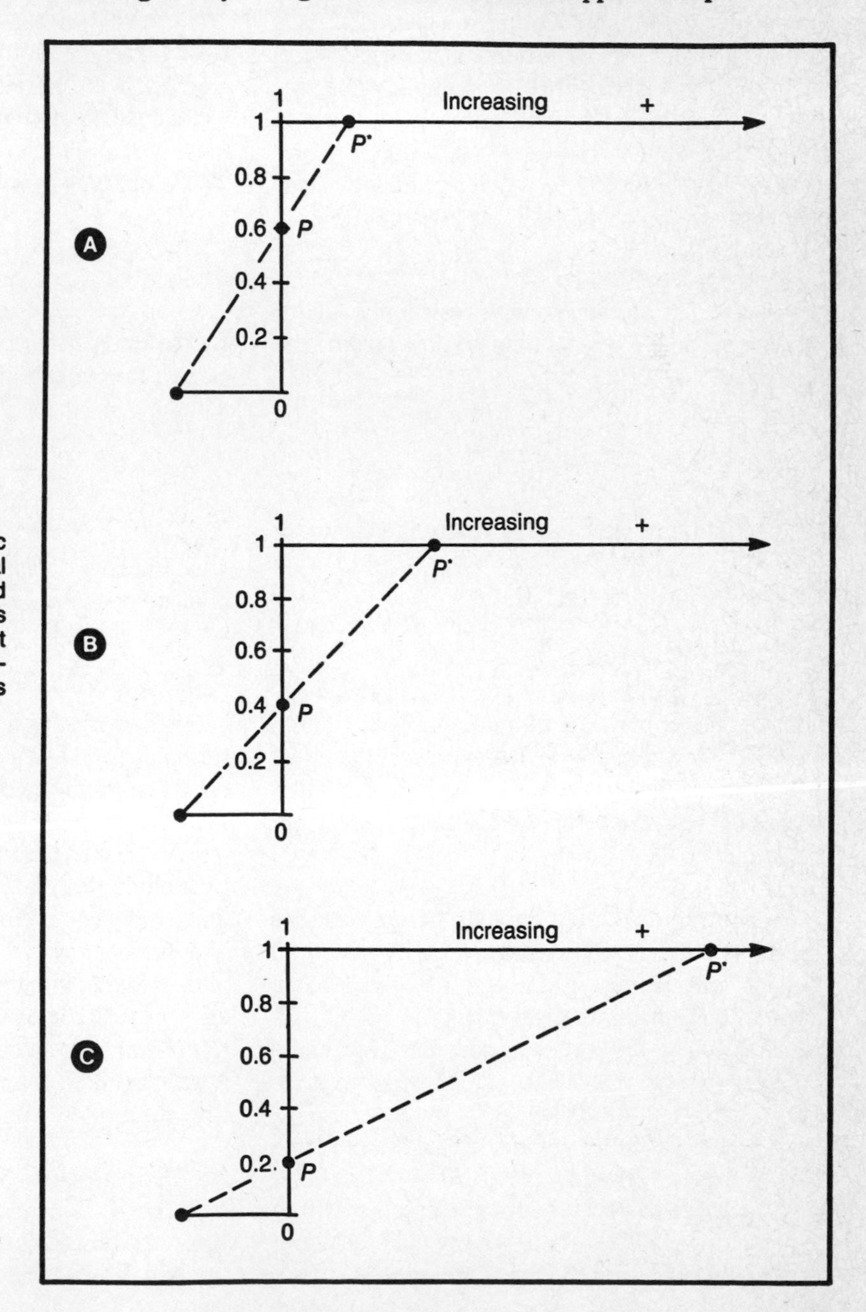

Fig. 6-4. Intuitive geometric representation of how the reciprocal of a number seems to vanish toward infinity as the number approaches 0. At A, $p = 0.6$; at B, $p = 0.4$; at C, $p = 0.2$. The point p^* goes off toward the right without limit as p gets close to 0.

finity." Let us imagine that the value of 1/0 is some mysterious entity, not letting ourselves get too sure that it really is "infinity." Let's call this entity I, perhaps to stand for "imaginary," "impossible," or "indescribable."

We should note that 1/0 does not mean "one divided by zero." To say this implies that $(I)(0) = 1$, and this is not true. The ratio operation is the same as division only if the denominator is nonzero, or, in the case of an entity of multiple value, the master set of the denominator entity does not contain zero.

Another thing to note is that we cannot be certain, until we prove it, that I is a real entity.

Propositon 6-10. $(+R)/0 = I$.

Proof. Let x be any positive real number. Then $1/x$ is also a positive real. This is known from real-number theory. Therefore,

$$\frac{x}{0} = \frac{x}{0/(1/x)}$$

By the Ratio Axiom, we can rearrange this to

$$\frac{x(1/x)}{0}$$

by letting $x = a$, $0 = b$, and $1/x = c$ in the statement of the axiom. For all real numbers x, $x(1/x) = 1$, and therefore the above expression is equal to 1. It thus follows that for all positive real numbers x, $x/0 = I$. Therefore $(+R)/0 = I$, the desired result.

Some interesting results follow from this. We can prove from the above that any entity having all positive real values will behave just like 1 when taken to ratio 0. For example, $(1,2,3,4,\ldots)/0 = I$, and $(2,6,7)/0 = I$. No matter how small we make the positive real, the result is still I when we take that number to ratio 0.

We now naturally wonder about the negative reals. We can easily show that if $1/0 = I$, then $-1/0 = -I$; and we can then prove in the same way as above that $(-R)/0 = -I$. Is $-I$ any different from I? The answer is no.

Proposition 6-11. $+I = -I$. That is, the sign we affix to I is of no importance.

Proof. We already know that $+I = 1/0$ if we agree that I means the same thing as $+I$ (just as $1 = +1$). Then

$$-I = -(+I) = -(1/0) = -1/0$$

Now we accept that whatever I may be, it must be true that $I = I$ because absolute equality is reflexive. Consequently, $1/0 = 1/0$. We also know that for any real number x not equal to zero, $0/x = 0$. Therefore, $0/-1 = 0$. We can now say that

$$\frac{1}{0} = \frac{1}{0/-1}$$

By the Ratio Axiom, we can change the right-hand side of this equation so that

$$1/0 = \frac{(1)(-1)}{0} = -1/0 = -I$$

which means that $I = -I$. The sign we affix to I is of no consequence.

FACTS INVOLVING I

We can prove a few facts involving this mysterious entity I, which shares with zero the property that it is its own negative. No positive or negative real number has this property. We might almost imagine the set of reals as being represented by a circle (Fig. 6-5) if we are willing to use a geometrically compressed scale where points are halfway further toward the end with each increasing or decreasing integer. The linear scheme is shown at A, where 1 is halfway to I from 0, 2 is halfway to I from 1, and so on, and exactly the same for the negatives. The complete circle is shown at B, and this is in fact a more accurate representation.

Proposition 6-12. $0/I = 0$.

Proof. Because $I = 1/0$, $0/I = 0/(1/0)$. By the Ratio Axiom, this is equivalent to $0(0/1)$. Because $0/1 = 0$, the expression becomes $(0)(0)$, which is 0.

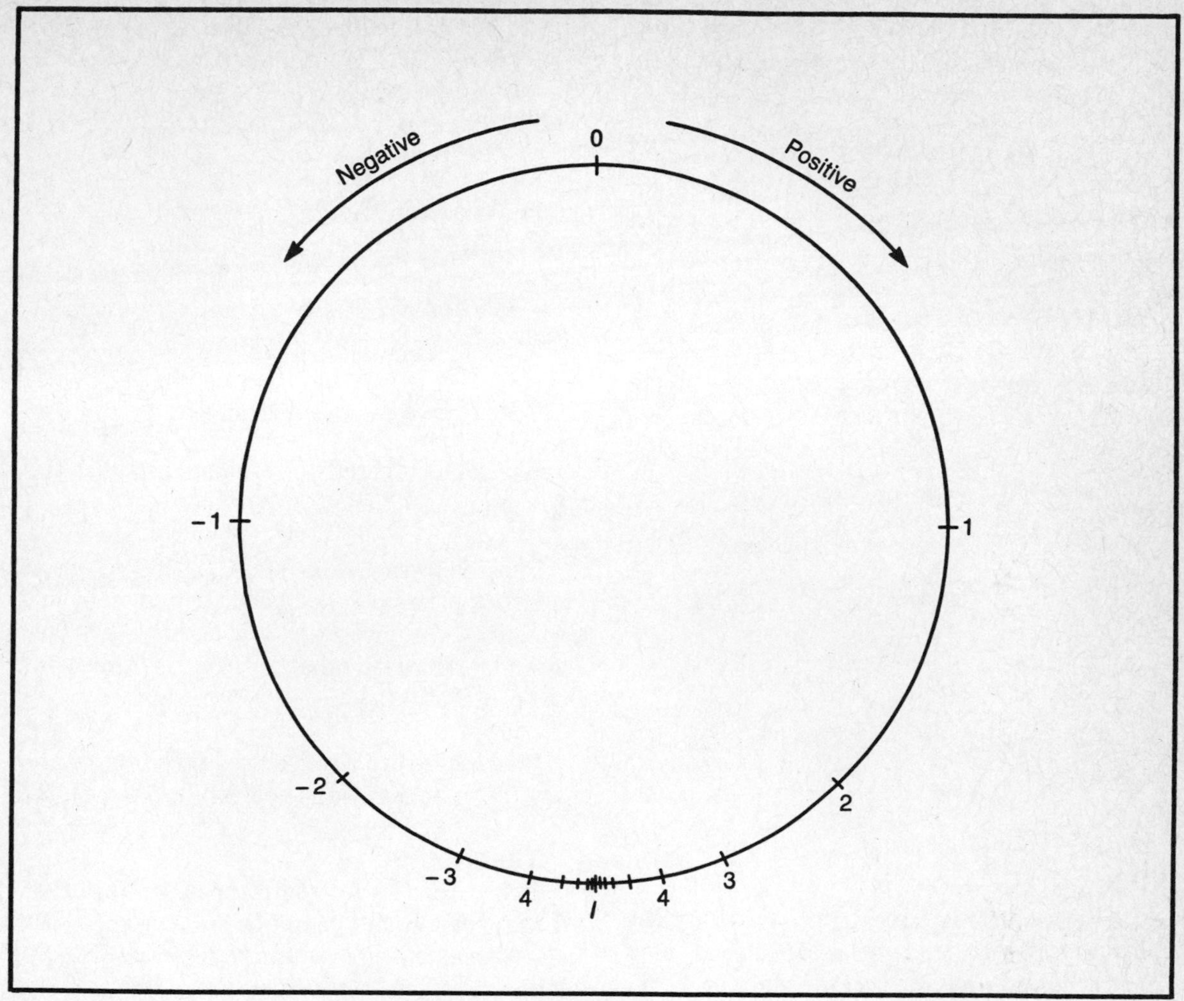

Fig. 6-5. Circular representation of the real numbers including I.

Proposition 6-13. $(+R)/I = (-R)/I = 0$.

Proof. By definition of I, $(+R)/I = (+R)/(1/0)$. By the Ratio Axiom,

$$\frac{(+R)}{1/0} = \frac{(+R)(0)}{1},$$

which reduces to 0/1, and this is 0. The proof for $(-R)$ results from replacing every occurrence of "+" in the above proof by "−".

Proposition 6-14. $I/(R) = I$.

Proof. This proof also hinges on the Ratio Axiom:

$$\frac{I}{(R)} = \frac{I}{(R)/1} = \frac{1}{(R)/I} = \frac{1}{0} = I$$

The entity, R, is, as previously said, the combination of values of all real numbers including zero. The Ratio Axiom is used, and then Propositions 6-12 and 6-13 are employed to reduce the expression to 1/0.

Proposition 6-15. $I(+R) = I(-R) = I$.

Proof. By the Ratio Axiom,

$$I(+R) = (1/0)(+R) = (+R)/0$$

By Proposition 6-10, $(+R)/0 = I$, and thus $I(+R) = I$. For the case of $(-R)$, we again use the Ratio Axiom to show that

$$I(-R) = (1/0)(-R) = (-R)/0$$

But $(-R)/0 = -[(+R)/0] = -I$. By Proposition 6-11, $-I = +I = I$.

Proposition 6-16. $(I)(I) = I$.

Proof. We need only prove the part for $+I$ because simple sign manipulation prooves the proposition in general. We may say

$$(+I)(+I) = (+I)(1/0)$$

Then, by the Ratio Axiom, we can change this expression to

$$(+I)(1/0) = \frac{1}{0/(+I)}$$

By Proposition 6-12, $0/(+I) = 0$, making the final expression 1/0, or $+I$.

THE VALUE OF I

Up to this time we have defined the entity I as simply the value 1/0, and generalized this to entail positive and negative reals in the place of 1. But we still aren't clear as to how its value relates to the real numbers. We cannot yet say that $I > 3$, for example, or that $I < -3$. In fact, if $+I$ and $-I$ are equal, all inequalities fail unless we consider $I = 0$. But this seems to be entirely contrary to all intuition. If $I \neq 0$, then I is not a real number. As previously said, we are tempted to think that I is "infinity" and that the limit of $1/x$, as x approaches zero, grows without bound. We can show that this notion leads to a false conclusion, based on our two axioms. The limit does increase without bound, but this says nothing at all about the actual value of $1/x$ when $x = 0$. A discontinuity occurs at this point in the function $I(x) = 1/x$.

Proposition 6-17. $I - I = 0/0$.

Proof. This is extremely simple, involving the progression

$$I - I = \frac{1}{0} + \frac{-1}{0} = \frac{1-1}{0} = \frac{0}{0}$$

Proposition 6-18. $I - I = I$.

Proof. We can say that $I = 2/0$ and $I = 1/0$, because $I = (+R)/0$ by the results of Proposition 6-10. Hence, $I - I = 2/0 - 1/0$. By the Addition Axiom.

$$2/0 - 1/0 = (2-1)/0 = 1/0 = I$$

We can use these two results to establish the following proposition.

Proposition 6-19. $0/0 = I$.

Proof. This follows immediately from the following two. Because $I - I = I$ and $I - I = 0/0$, and we know trivially that $I - I = I - I$, the conclusion is that $0/0 = I$.

Now we are in a position to easily prove the primary theorem that we have been building up to.

Theorem 6-1. $I = 0$.

Proof. We know from Proposition 6-19 that $0/0 = I$. Then, from Proposition 6-13, we know that $1/I = 0$ because $(+R)/I = 0$ and 1 is a value of $(+R)$. Thus,

$$\frac{1}{0/0} = 1/I = 0$$

By the Ratio Axiom,

$$\frac{1}{0/0} = \frac{(1)(0)}{0} = 0/0 = I$$

But now we have this expression, $\frac{1}{(0/0)}$, which is absolutely equal to both 0 and I! Because absolute equality is transitive according to Proposition 6-2, it follows that $0 = I$.

This is truly a bizarre result. What we might intuitively have been thinking of as "infinity" really

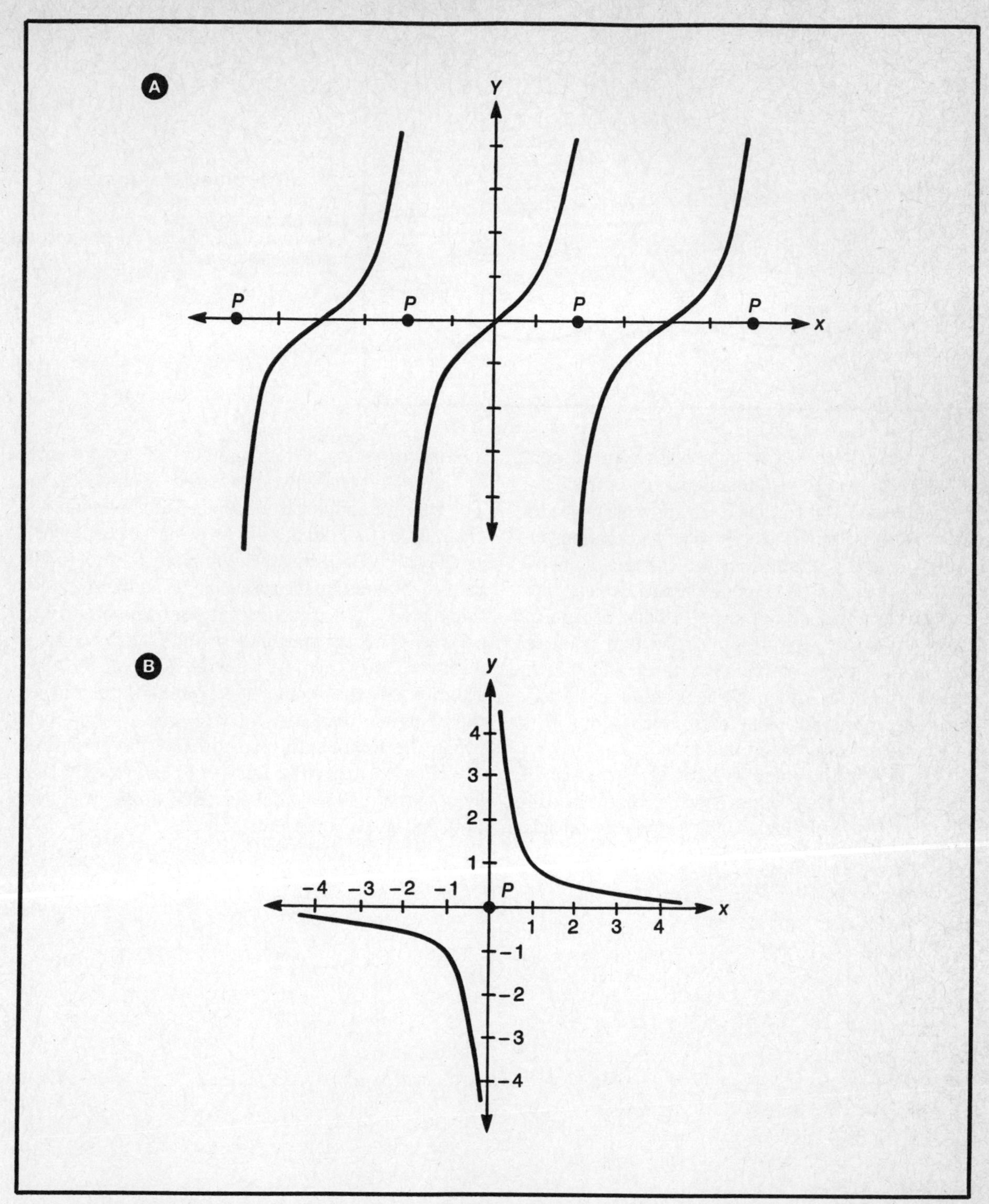

Fig. 6-6. Adding points *p* to functions containing singularities in order to make them defined over the domain of all reals. At A, $y = \tan x$; at B, $y = 1/x$.

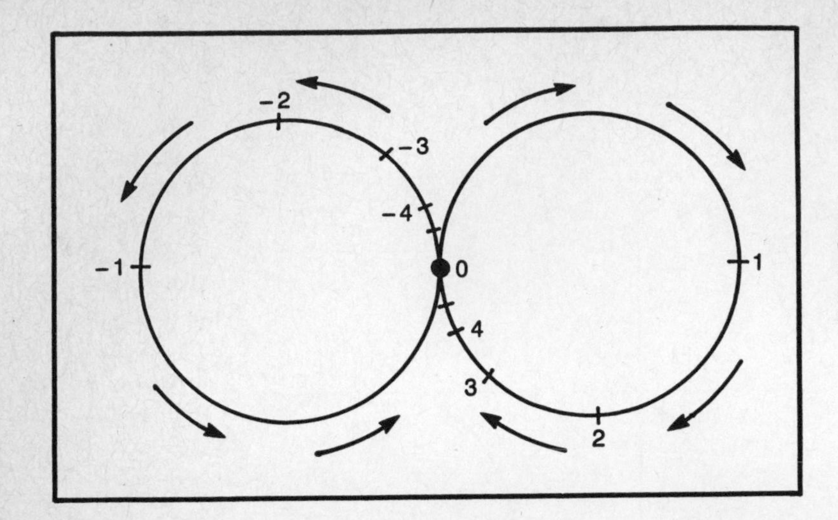

Fig. 6-7. Figure-eight representation of the real numbers. There is no infinity among them, yet the whole set is defined over all four basic arithmetic operations.

turns out to be zero! And as odd as this may seem, it does not seem to lead to any major contradiction in mathematical formulas if we allow this to be the case. At least this is true insofar as functions are concerned. We might consider the trigonometric functions such as the tangent function, which "blow up" at certain points, and put a point at zero for each singularity. Figure 6-6 shows two examples of this; at A is the function $y = \tan x$, and at B the function $y = 1/x$. Although this does not make these functions continuous, it at least provides for a value at the points previously undefined.

So what is the point of all this? Is there a catch? And if not, so what? The answer is that it leads to some interesting thoughts. We might now consider the entire system of real numbers as being a sort of figure-eight when represented geometrically. The positive and negative numbers can be thought of as circles tangent at a single point. The singularity is represented by all the previously undefined values obtained by the ratio operation: that is, anything in which zero occurs in the denominator (Fig. 6-7). Maybe if we start at zero and go in a positive direction, infinitely far, we will end up at the singularity, and then come back from infinitely far in the negative, then back to zero, going round and round the figure-eight as shown by the arrows.

How odd that the figure-eight is exactly the symbol that has so long been used, from antiquity until today, to represent infinity.

Chapter 7

Anomalies in the Physical World

THE PURE MATHEMATICIAN IS A THEORIST. ALL he or she really needs is a pencil, a few pieces of paper (a dime-store notebook will usually be enough for plenty of scribbling), a clear head and someplace quiet in which to think. Albert Einstein was a theorist; he worked out his early theories in the privacy of a barren little room in a rooming house in Switzerland, after hours. The pure experimentalist is just the opposite. This person sets up apparatus and makes observations and measurements under various conditions, and leaves it up to others to draw the conclusions from data presented. A professor once told me, "One experimentalist can keep a dozen theorists busy," and this is true in physics if not in pure mathematics. The "real world" is so unreal, when dissected by modern science, as to render it almost beyond comprehension.

Most mathematical theories have some application to physics. Calculus, for example, can be used to figure out the speed of a spaceship or the intensity of an electromagnetic field. Vector analysis is used in navigation. Almost every aspect of mathematics, and a good bit of philosophy, too, is involved in figuring out the structure of our universe, both in the large sense (outer space) and the small (inner space).

PARTICLES WITHOUT END

In the last century, physicists began to realize that matter is not solid stuff, the way it looks to us as we casually observe it, but instead is grainy, in the sense that it is made up of billions upon billions of tiny, moving particles. We call these particles molecules. Every conceivable kind of material thing is comprised of molecules that are so small that even a typical, store-bought microscope cannot resolve them.

Later, it was discovered that molecules themselves are made up of even tinier particles. These were called atoms, the fundamental constituents of the universe. Some molecules have just one atom, and many have two atoms. Some molecules have more than two atoms, hooked together in some way that to us, as mathematicians, is not very important. But nonetheless it is interesting because this strange arrangement of incomprehensibly miniscule things is what actually makes things happen in our cosmos.

Atoms themselves are like little solar systems, in a sense. The most commonly known models of the atom, still taught at the elementary school level, are the Rutherford and Bohr models. Positively charged nuclei have little negatively charged things orbiting them, according to these ideas; and because negative attracts positive, the centrifugal force of the orbiting "electrons" exactly balances the positive charge of the nuclei. The electrons orbit at various distances from the nuclei. Some nuclei have a lot of positive charge and there are many electrons going around them. Some nuclei have less charge and correspondingly fewer electrons. Usually, the negative and positive electrical charges in an atom are equal, so that the whole atom carries a net electrical charge of zero. Sometimes there is an excess of negative charge, or an excess of positive charge. This might happen because of an overabundance of electrons, or because of a deficiency, respectively. Atoms can join together when they share electrons. It gets quite complicated, but it can all be explained very nicely in terms of negative electrons, positive protons, and neutral particles called neutrons.

A model of the water (H_2O) molecule is shown in Fig. 7-1. Today, we know that this representation is a greatly simplified one. The oxygen atom has eight electrons in two "shells" which are really nothing but probability spaces indicating that any given electron will be inside the sphere half the time and outside the sphere half the time. We show the spheres as circles in this illustration, and show the electrons as orbiting at a constant distance from the nucleus. The simpler hydrogen atoms have just one electron going around one proton. The second, or outer, oxygen electron shell has, for some reason, a desire to have eight electrons, and a free oxygen atom has only six electrons in the outer shell. We don't know exactly why, but this is what the experimentalists tell us. By sharing electrons with two hydrogen atoms, the outer shell of the oxygen atom is in a sense "satisfied" and thus the water molecule is stable. It does not readily react with very

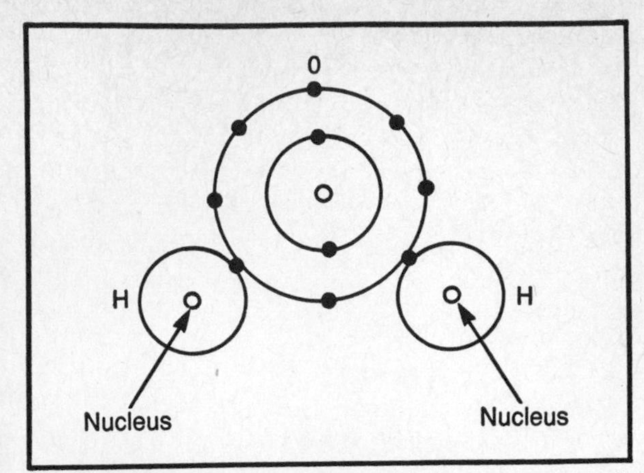

Fig. 7-1. Example of a molecule, in this case water, in which atoms share electrons. This illustration is greatly simplified.

many other substances. Pure oxygen is much more reactive, and is responsible for corrosion on copper, brass, iron, and other metals.

In fact the situation is far more complicated than Fig. 7-1, so much more goes on that we can't even begin to illustrate it by means of a drawing. The protons (eight), neutrons (eight) and electrons (eight) in an oxygen atom, and the proton and electron in a hydrogen atom, are themselves made up of smaller constituents known as *quarks*. The term, quark, comes from the book *Finnegan's Wake* by James Joyce. Perhaps the physicists were looking for a totally arbitrary name for these particles. It seems that so many different kinds of particles have recently been, and are continuing to be, discovered that we are running out of names for them. Matter is so complex that we might repeat what one ancient king said long ago about the epicycle model of the solar system: he remarked that if he had been present at the creation, he might have given some advice to God! Contrast this with Einstein: God may be sophisticated but he is not malicious. I myself sometimes wonder whether or not the creator might be laughing up his sleeve at us as we try to keep track of the structure of the cosmos.

The experimentalists have plenty to work on when it comes to figuring out how matter is put together, and how energy and matter are interrelated. The physical theorists busily try to construct models that fit observed facts and, hopefully, give the experimentalists an idea as to what they should look for next. One of the most bizarre particles that theorists have discovered in their blackboards full of formulas is the *tachyon*. It has not actually been found yet, but supposedly it travels faster than the speed of light, an impossibility in this universe according to the principles of relativity. There are the neutrinos, particles with zero mass but somehow still having "spin." These particles have in fact been observed via experiment; they can penetrate the entire planet Earth as easily as a beam of light can pass through a thin pane of glass. No doubt more particles will be found, and this process of uncovering new, mysterious particles may well continue for as long as we have physicists to look for them.

Enter the mathematician and philosopher. The physicists can keep on digging, plugging away, making new discoveries. Let us, the pure theoreticians, retire to the privacy of our ivory tower and daydream.

"Suppose," says our professor, "that there are infinitely many different kinds of particles in the universe."

Then the physicists will never find them all.

"Or suppose that the structure of matter is ultimately just one kind of particle, with zero volume and the same density as the universe all told."

What does this mean?

"We know the universe has a certain density," continues the professor. "There is some dispute as to exactly what it is, but imagine, for the sake of discussion, that it is equivalent to one mid-sized American-made car every thousand cubic miles." That's a pretty strange way to put it, but we give the mentor his time.

"We can break this down further. Perhaps there are 5,000 baseball weights to this particular kind of car. Then the universe has the density of 5,000 baseballs per thousand cubic miles, or five baseballs per cubic mile."

Well, we mutter, all right.

"If we keep breaking this down, say into marbles, with 20 marbles to the baseball, the universe can be said to have a density of 100 marbles per cubic mile. It is still the same density as the universe made up of baseballs or cars, but there are more particles of a smaller size.

"Keep going. Say there are three lead shot to a marble, or 10,000 grains of sand to a marble. We might say that the universe has a density of 300 lead shot, or 1,000,000 grains of sand, per cubic mile, and we would still be talking about the same density."

What's he getting at?

"This process can be continued without limit. We can break things down into bits of dust, molecules, atoms, elementary particles—if there is such a thing as an elementary particle—and have the density remain the same.

"Of course the universe is not uniform in density. Matter is clumped into galactic clusters, individual galaxies, stars, planets, asteroids, and smaller rocks or meteors flying through space. These objects are made up of molecules and atoms, and protons, neutrons, and electrons make up the atoms. Quarks make up all of the protons, neutrons, and electrons. And we mustn't forget the role that energy plays in the mass of the universe. We have photons, perhaps tachyons, and even the massless neutrino that does not affect the density of the universe but nevertheless is there."

Okay, but so what?

"We may someday discover quarks to be made up of tinier particles, and these constructed from still tinier ones. Imagine, if you will, that matter could be made up of infinitely many particles, all infinitely small, and having density of infinite magnitude. Suppose that ultimately, matter is either all there, or not there at all!"

Now you are wondering, has this man lost his mind?

"Mathematically, we can approach this situation, as we see in the drawing (Fig. 7-2). As the particles get smaller, their density increases without limit, if we are to maintain a constant overall density in the cosmos. If the particle volume were zero, the density would have to be infinite. This is a concept that the experimentalists can never verify nor disprove. Let them keep looking and looking for that fundamental particle. If our daydream is true, they'll never find it!"

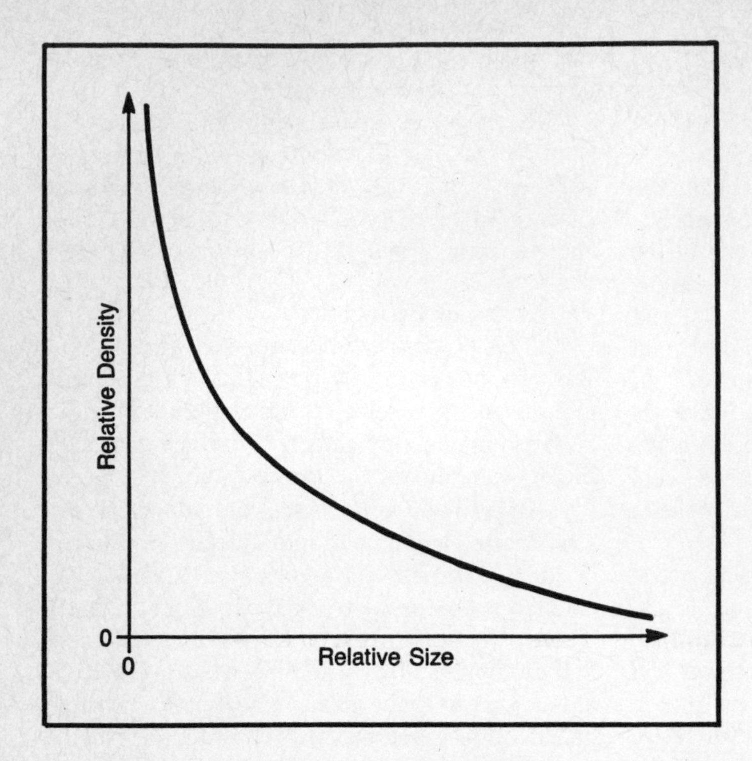

Fig. 7-2. Perhaps the density of a particle increases without limit as its size approaches zero.

At this point we leave the good professor to ruminate in his private world. What if he is right? As we leave the ivory tower for the humdrum world, we might almost imagine that we see the professor chuckling to himself.

ORDER FROM RANDOMNESS

Whether or not the foregoing idea is really the true structure of the universe, we do know that there are an awful lot of particles, and they are constantly moving. This motion was first observed under microscopes, as small objects such as bacteria appeared to vibrate for no apparent reason. This motion, evidently random, was called Brownian motion after its discoverer. The motion was believed to result from impacts of still smaller, unseen particles. These were the molecules. The theory that these tiny particles existed was ultimately proven correct.

Molecules, atoms, electrons, and even protons and neutrons, are in constant motion. The motion becomes more vigorous as the temperature gets higher. The physicists tell us this is because the particles have more kinetic energy at higher temperatures as compared with lower temperatures. This motion is enormously complex. With all these billions of particles moving around and occasionally bumping into each other, we cannot predict where a given particle will be at a given time. The motion is simply too complex. We can say, in the case of an electron, what the probability is that it will be within a certain distance of the nucleus of an atom; we can estimate the probability that a given atom will be within a certain designated space at a certain time. But exact predictions are too complicated. In theory, however, it should be possible to predict the position of any particle at any time, because there are only finitely many particles—right?

Not if the idea proposed by our mad professor has any credibility. If there are infinitely many particles, we could never, ever predict where any one of them would be at a given time. To do this would require calculations of infinite complexity, or taking up an infinite amount of time. We might have to resolve infinite series of horrible complexity. Even the tiniest error might mean a mistake of major proportions; we all know how a small miscalculation can have a tremendous impact on the results of an experiment or observation.

If there are finitely many particles in the universe, the randomness of motion is almost, but not quite, complete. This would be consistent with the idea, proposed in Chapter 1, that there might not be such a thing as true randomness. But if there are infinitely many particles, their motion might indeed be truly random.

Whether the randomness of inner-space motion is true or almost perfect, we know that as the scale grows larger, the order becomes more and more easy to see. Although we cannot, by present technology, say exactly where a certain electron will be at a certain time, we can easily say where a chair will be if we don't move it. It is not likely that all the atoms in a chair will move two feet towards the northwest, all at once. (It is statistically possible, but the probability is extremely small.) We can say with almost perfect confidence that when we leave our desk to get a glass of water, the desk will be in the same place, with the papers arranged in the same way, as when we left, barring interference from a nosy coworker or a fan running at too high a speed. On a larger scale, we can predict the seasons with great certainty because the earth orbits the sun in a predictable way. We can say that the sun will be about the same size and temperature tomorrow as it is today, although astronomers might remind us that this is not true of all stars. Our Milky Way galaxy is still more stable. Although individual stars actually do blow up once in a while, the whole galaxy almost certainly won't.

On the scale of the whole universe, there is some doubt as to whether or not it is all that stable. There are two prevailing theories concerning the evolution of the universe: the steady-state theory and the big-bang theory.

The steady-state theory is the notion that the density of the universe is constant with time, and that things always have been and always will be about the same as they are now. If things appear to get more and more stable with increasing size—randomness having less and less observable an effect—then this theory is consistent with what we see. The ultimate "order" in the universe should exist on the largest scale, just as the least order is on the smallest scale.

The big-bang theory holds that the universe had a beginning, in the form of a violent explosion. Everything was, according to this theory, contained in one point of space, or a tiny particle of phenomenal density. For some reason this particle, called the "primordial fireball" or "ylem," exploded and formed all the matter in the universe. This theory would imply that the universe changes in size with time, constantly expanding as a result of this blowup. The Doppler shift in the light coming from far-off galaxies, a shift toward lower frequency and longer wavelength with increasing distance, is consistent with the idea that the universe is getting larger and larger with time. If the big-bang theory is correct, the density of the universe is decreasing. The beginning, incredibly hot and dense, would gradually give way to a cold, sparse, dark end, or, if gravity were sufficient, to eventual collapse and perhaps another blowup.

Both of these theories defines an ultimate state of order. The steady-state theory, envisioned by the astronomer Fred Hoyle and others, is appealing because it implies an eternal state of things; the big-bang theory, propounded by George Gamow and others, appeals to some because of the attractiveness of an ultimate origin in time and because of its glorious drama. The near-randomness of the tiny gives way to an orderly, if perhaps violent, state of affairs in the totality of the cosmos.

Unless, of course, one of Carl Sagan's daydreams is true: our universe might be an elementary particle in some hyper-universe of incredibly huge dimensions. Then we are right back to where we started from. The total order would be reduced to the ultimate randomness.

THE STRUCTURE OF THE UNIVERSE

We say that space is three-dimensional. This means that, in order to uniquely define the position of any point, we need three numbers or coordinates. There are several different arrangements that are used to define the position of an object in space. We may use angles and distances, or just displacement numbers. Three different methods are shown in Fig. 7-3.

The method at A shows a Cartesian three-space. We need an origin and three axes, usually oriented at right angles to each other and called the *x*, *y*, and *z* axes. A point is defined with respect to the origin by means of three numbers *x*, *y*, and *z*, forming what is called the *ordered triple*, (*x*,*y*,*z*). Each

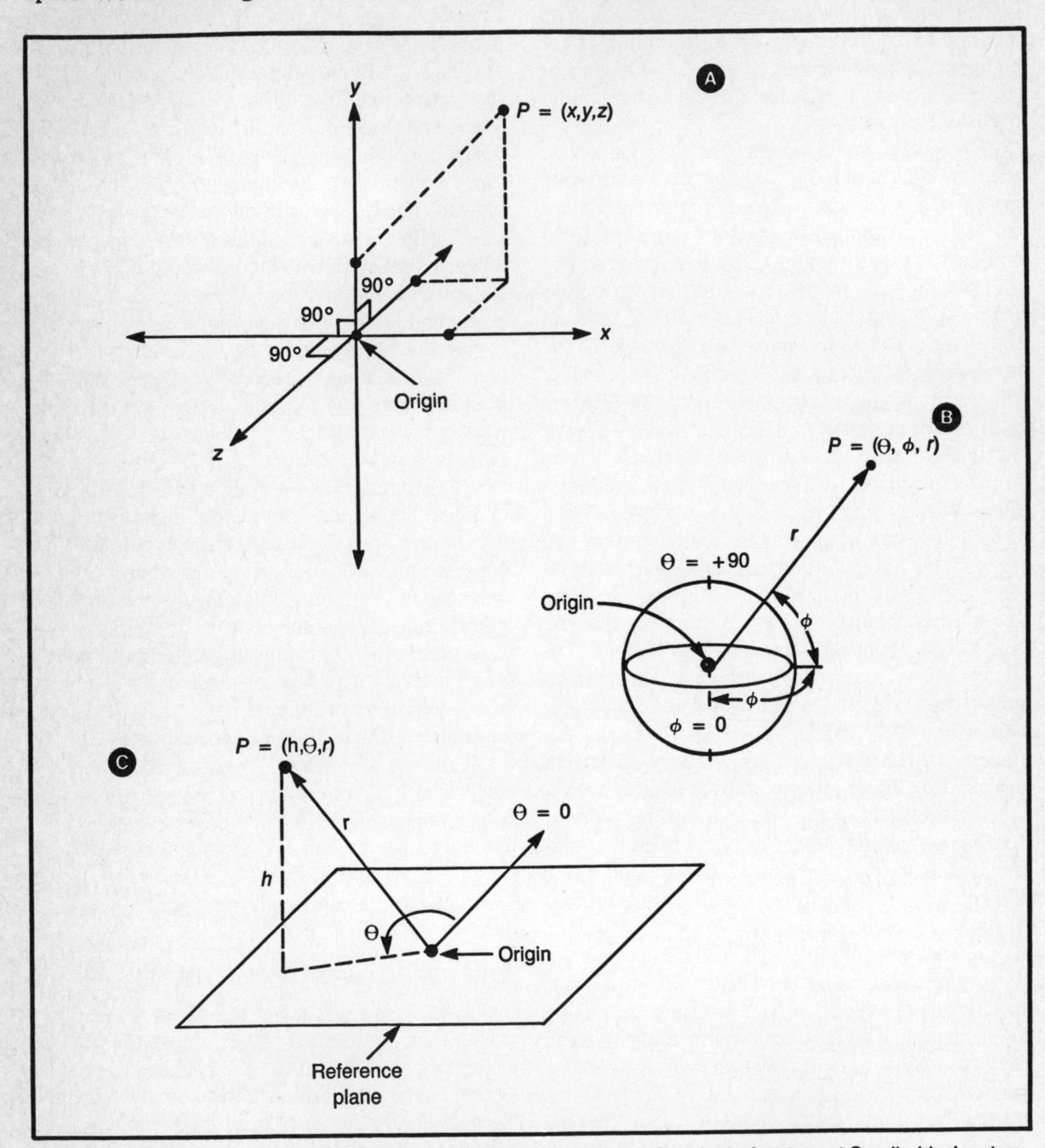

Fig. 7-3. Three-dimensional coordinate systems. At A, Cartesian system; at B, spherical system; at C, cylindrical system. Coordinate designators are discussed in the text. In each case, a point is shown, labeled *P*.

point in space corresponds to exactly one ordered triple, and each ordered triple corresponds to exactly one point in space. The set of ordered triples (x,y,z), where x, y, and z are real numbers, is homomorphic with the set of all points in three-space.

The method at B uses spherical coordinates. This method might be likened to the latitudes and longitudes on the surface of the earth, plus a third value, the radial distance. If we consider latitude to be θ, longitude to be ϕ, and radius to be r, then every point in space corresponds to a point (θ,ϕ,r). The values of θ, ϕ and r do not, in this system, cover all of the real numbers. If we use degrees for the angle measure, the latitude θ might range from -90 (south pole) to $+90$ (north pole), the longitude ϕ from 0 to 360 or from -180 to $+180$, and the radius from 0 on upward without limit.

The method at C illustrates cylindrical coordinates. In this system we define a height h, a compass angle θ, and a radial distance r. The value of h can be any real number, with the negatives being downward and the positives being upward. The compass angle ranges from 0 to 360 and the radius r from 0 upward without limit. Each point in three-space can be defined by an ordered triple (h,θ,r).

Geometry in three-space is considerably more complicated, and more difficult to envision, than geometry in two-space. Drawings on flat paper must sacrifice clarity so that it is possible to see any rendition of the object or process at all. Modern computers have graphic displays that allow an observer to "see" a three-dimensional object from various different angles, so that it looks much more real than any drawing made on plain paper. A special method of photography, known as holography, works in a similar way. But true three-dimensional drawings just don't exist. We have to use sculpture and this can be impossible for extremely complicated objects having surfaces inside one another.

It doesn't normally occur to us that there might be more than three dimensions. In the world of mathematics, though, we are not limited by physical constraints. We might have four, five, or even six geometric dimensions—or perhaps even infinitely many. A four-space would require four coordinate values to uniquely determine the position of a point; a five-space would require five coordinates, and so on. There would be many possible methods of finding the position of a point in a many-dimensioned universe. The easiest to imagine, and the most commonly used, is an extension of the Cartesian idea.

Let's go back to the idea of a two-space. This might be a plane or the surface of any smooth object. Suppose we have little creatures on this two-dimensional surface. Their movements are limited compared to what we are used to.

Imagine one of these two-dimensional creatures, imprisoned inside a square (Fig. 7-4). He cannot get out. But it is easy for us to think of a way to get him out: reach in, grab him, yank him off the two-dimensional surface that is his universe, and plop him down outside the square! So easy for us, but impossible for him, or anyone else in his universe that might be trying to help him escape without breaking the square.

We can extend this idea to our own universe. Suppose that somebody is locked in a cubicle that cannot be broken open. There is no escape unless the walls are breached. But a four-dimensional being, looking at this poor three-space person, could quite easily grab him and pull him out without the

Fig. 7-4. In two dimensions, a square could imprison a hypothetical being. We could easily envision how to get him out, but he is helpless to escape nor even see how it could possibly be done.

walls of the cubicle even being touched. We cannot envision how this could be done, but mathematically it could be, if we allow four dimensions to exist.

There is another way a person could escape from the cubicle, and this method is more easy for us to imagine. Suppose that time travel were possible, both forward and backward. Then if you were imprisoned in a sealed chamber, you could go forward in time until the structure rotted or was dismantled. Then you would simply walk a few feet, go back in time, and be outside the enclosure! Alternatively you could zip back in time to a point before the structure was built; walk a few meters, go forward in time, and you'd be outside the cubicle. If the cubicle were transparent you might be surprised if you went too far back in time (in the first case) or not far enough ahead (in the second case) to return: you'd see yourself in the cubicle from the outside, and outside the cubicle from the inside—at the same time. Figure *that* out.

Physicists and astronomers often talk of time as the fourth dimension. But they also entertain the possibility that there might exist a fourth geometric dimension. How do they get any evidence to support this idea? The evidence comes from the observational verification of a mathematical theory that three-space is "curved." Just as a two-dimensional surface can be curved with respect to three-space (imagine a basketball or the earth, for example), three-space can be curved with respect to four-space. Einstein predicted that this curvature could be detected by means of precise astronomical observations and it was.

This idea that space is curved is based on the theory's ability to explain the observed facts. Einstein demonstrated that light coming from distant stars would be "bent" by the curvature of space in the gravitational field of the sun (Fig. 7-5). This was to be a very tiny curvature, not very much—but noticeable by means of telescopes. The observed curvature was in agreement with Einstein's prediction. Within experimental error, theory and observed data coincided.

Space that is "curved," or non-Euclidean, has some odd properties. The shortest distance between two points is not necessarily a straight line. How would you get from your house to Moscow? The shortest path you could take would be curved unless you were willing to do a lot of digging. In a non-Euclidean three-space, the same idea applies.

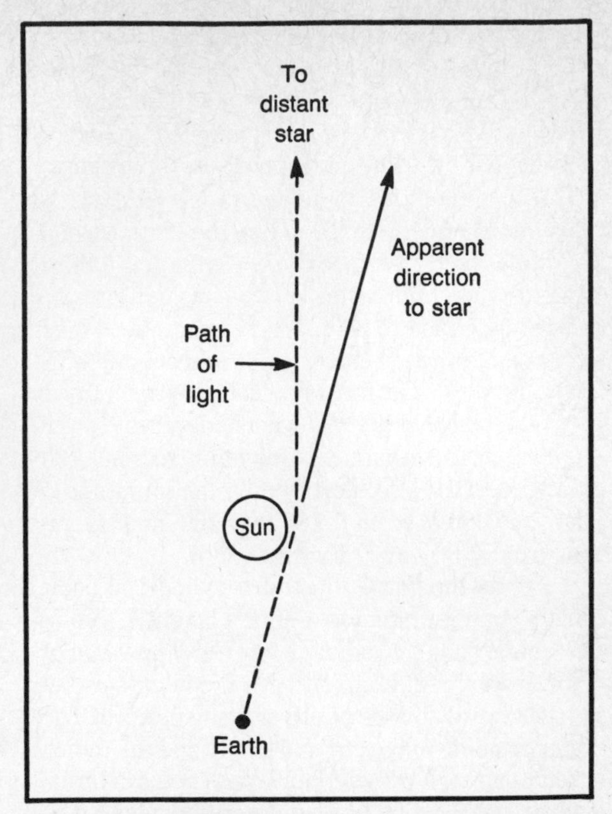

Fig. 7-5. The gravitational field of the sun causes curvature in the path of a light beam from a distant star, changing the apparent position of the star in space. (This drawing shows the effect greatly exaggerated.)

The curvature of three-space implies, logically, that four dimensions do exist. If any n-space is non-Euclidean, the logical consequence is that there exists an $n+1$-space. (You can think of this in terms of the idea that a two-dimensional, spherical surface requires three dimensions.) The question then comes to us: how many dimensions are there? We at first thought there were three. But now we have evidence to the effect that there are four, because three-space is not "flat." Could four-space, too, be non-Euclidean? We do not know. Even Einstein could not tell us this, although if asked, he might have said that any space could be non-Euclidean. If this open-minded approach is true (and in mathematics anything can be true as long as it is logically consistent), then there is no limit to the number of dimensions that can exist.

Let's modify our thought about dimensionality so as to be more specific. We can propose a definition as follows:

Definition. A space has n dimensions if, and only if, it is possible to place exactly n straight rods with their ends touching, in such a way so that each rod is perpendicular to all of the others.

Examples of this for two and three dimensions are shown in Fig. 7-6A and B.

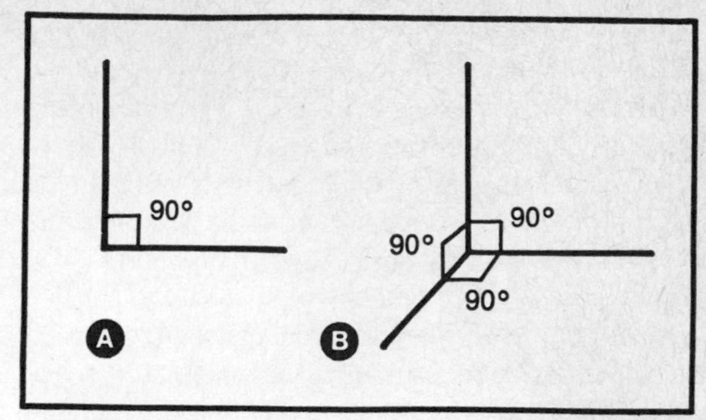

Fig. 7-6. In n dimensions, it is possible to place exactly n straight rods end-to-end so that they are mutually perpendicular. Here, this is shown for two dimensions (A) and three dimensions (B).

We cannot place four rods together in this way in our three-space. In a four-space we could, but envisioning this is impossible for us. We might think of time as a fourth dimension, and then we could consider the progress of time to be "perpendicular" to three-space, and therefore perpendicular to all three rods placed together so that they are mutually orthogonal. This principle can be used to make "time-space drawings" of objects that appear and disappear. Any rendition of five-space is impossible for us to directly make, even with the addition of time as a dimension. Higher spaces are likewise more difficult. Nonetheless we can use the preceding definition to set up Cartesian coordinate systems for spaces of any number of dimensions; the perpendicular rods are extended infinitely in both directions for each, and values assigned along the axes. When this is done, a point in n-space can be uniquely defined by an ordered n-tuple $(x_1,x_2,x_3, \ldots, x_n)$.

INFINITY-SPACE

How many dimensions can exist? We can mathematically define a space of any natural number of dimensions, and even a zero-space (point). There is no limit to the dimensionality of spaces. This gives rise to an interesting thought: can there be an infinity-space?

We might say no at first. In order to uniquely define a point in such a space, we would have to have an ordered "infinity-tuple" of numbers because there would be infinitely many axes, all mutually orthogonal and all having a coordinate value. An ordered "infinity-tuple" would be written

$$P = (x_1,x_2,x_3, \ldots)$$

where P is the point in question. The problem arises: how can we ever know all of the x_i values? We could never name them all; we couldn't read off this string of numbers if we had a trillion years! If we can't know the numbers, how can we know where in infinity-space the point is?

But there is a way we can know. We can know that the point does in fact exist, and that it is a unique point, even though we can't say for sure just where it is. The set of natural numbers is infinitely large, but we intuitively know the whole set. If we had a point in infinity-space, we can intuitively know that the set of coordinates does exist, even if we cannot know exactly what they all are. The universe of mathematics is more powerful than the universe of our imagination.

Let's go back now, for a moment, to the idea of non-Euclidean space. Consider the surface of the earth, and the distance from your home town to Moscow, USSR. This distance is on the order of a few thousand miles if you live in the United States. Think of the surface of the earth as a two-space, roughly shaped like a sphere except for small irregularities, and think of the distance you would have to travel in order to get from your driveway to the Kremlin. Then think of three-space, and the distance you would have to travel if you were able to dig your way through the interior of the earth.

The distance through the sphere is less than the distance over the surface. This would be true in any case except for a flat surface, when the shortest distance between two points would be on the surface itself. Fig. 7-7 shows three dimensionally-reduced illustrations of this. In any case where an n-space is curved, it is evident intuitively that the path between two points in n-space is longer than the path in $n+1$-space in practically every case. If the n-space is a "sphere"—a set of points equidistant from a single center point—then this principle holds for any two points on the "sphere." If our universe is non-Euclidean, and it is generally believed that it is, then the shortest distance between two points lies in four-space. Despite the difficulty of imagining a path shorter than a straight line, such a path exists, because "straight" lines in our universe aren't really straight.

Suppose now that four-space is non-Euclidean. Then an even shorter path between two fixed points exists in five-space. Let us call the points P and Q. If, in three-space, the distance between P and Q is one meter, it is a little less in four-space and a little smaller yet in five-space. We can illustrate this principle for a one-space (circle) and two-space (sphere) in our three-space; this is done in Fig. 7-8. The two points lie on a circle, and they are a given distance d_1 apart as measured around the circle. The circle lies on the surface of a sphere; the distance d_2 as measured over the surface of the sphere is smaller than d_1. If we measure the separation of P and Q in three-space—through the sphere—we obtain a still smaller distance, d_3. If three-space is the surface of a four-sphere, then there is a distance d_4, through four dimensions, that is smaller than d_3. We can go on with this progression without end. Imagine a structured infinity-space with subspaces, each of which are "n-spheres." We then have a progression of distances between P and Q:

$$d_1, d_2, d_3, \ldots, d_n, \ldots$$

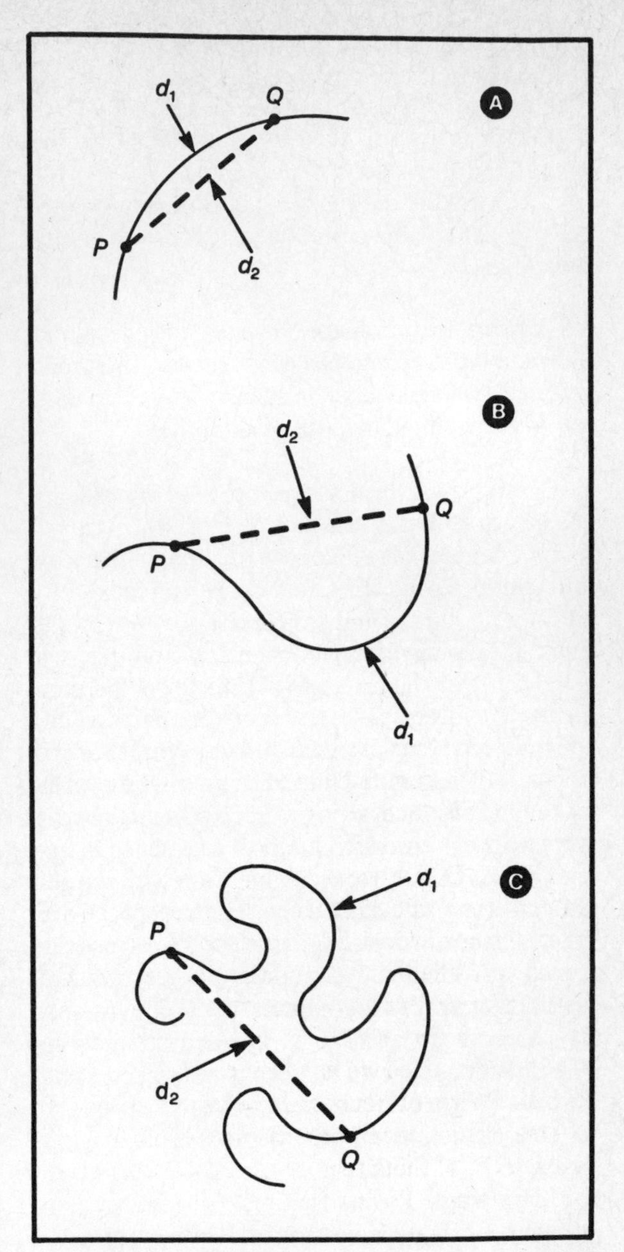

Fig. 7-7. Three examples of how the distance through two dimensions (d_2) might be shorter than the distance through one dimension (d_1). The drawings A, B, and C show progressively more complicated and dramatic examples.

with $d_1 > d_2 > d_3 > \ldots > d_n > \ldots$

The question now becomes, to what limiting value does d_n converge? This depends on the relative sizes of the n-spheres. The analysis is too com-

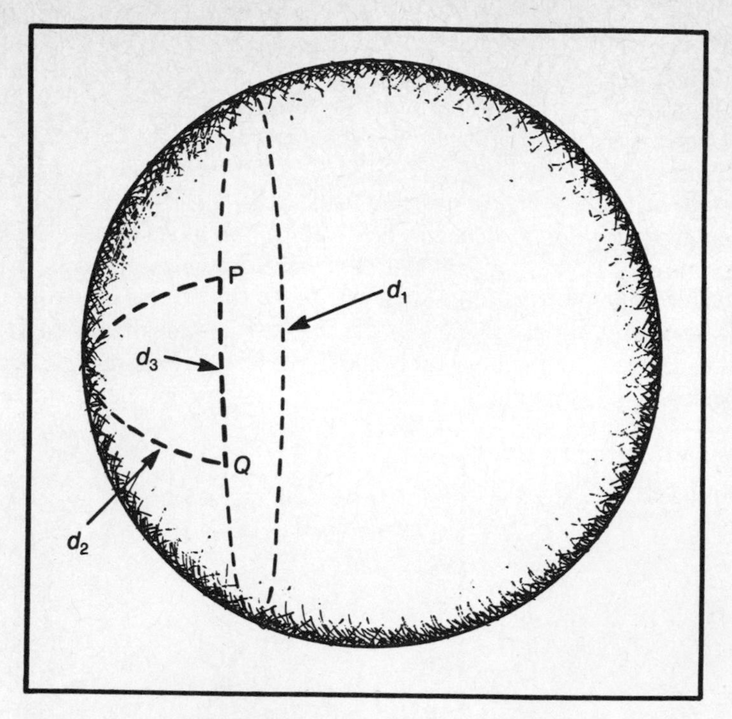

Fig. 7-8. Two points, *P* and *Q*, lie on a sphere, connected by a circle (dotted line). The distance over the circle is d_1. A great circle on the sphere (heavy dotted line) results in a smaller separation d_2. Measuring directly through the sphere (irregular heavy dotted line) gives the smallest distance, d_3.

plicated for discussion in detail here, but there might exist a combination of *n*-spheres that would cause the distance between any two points to converge toward zero as the number of dimensions is increased. If this were the case, then the whole infinity-space would in reality be a single point! The infinity-space would be a zero-space.

Could it be that our physical universe is actually structured this way? That would be an interesting thing to try and prove. We'll probably never really know, since we have no way of telling what the structure of four-space, five-space, and in general any *n*-space (for $n > 3$) is. But it is rather fun, isn't it, to think that we are all moving around within a single geometric point in infinity-space, where everything is nothing and nothing is everything. It is but a short intuitive step to apply this idea to time as well: all of this nothingness is taking place in a single instant.

BLACK HOLES

A more real, and already proven (mathematically, at least), anomaly in our three-space universe occurs because of intense gravitation. The more powerful a gravitational field, the greater the escape velocity becomes. The escape velocity is defined as that speed at which an object must be propelled directly upwards, in order to permanently get away from the gravitational field of a celestial body. The escape velocity for Earth is about 25,000 miles per hour, or about 7 miles per second, neglecting air resistance. If you could throw a baseball straight up at this speed, the ball would get out of the earth's field of gravity forever; it would never fall back again.

For a more dense planet, or a larger one, the escape velocity might be greater. It could be much greater. Conversely, for a small object such as an asteroid, the escape velocity is very low. In fact, on some asteroids, you could easily throw a baseball out of its gravitational field. You might even be able to jump up and fly away into space, never to fall back.

Suppose there were an object with an escape velocity so great that it was the speed of light—186,282 miles per second—or more. Then even a beam of light would not escape. Even photons of radiant energy would fall back to the surface of the object. Can this actually happen? Physicists generally think that it can. Such an object would be invisible because it would emit no light. But if you got caught in its gravitational field, you would feel the effects, and if you got too close, you would be captured by the field, and you would have absolutely no way whatsoever to get out again. This sort of anomaly in space is called a black hole.

The idea of a black hole is not really all that new. Scientists thought up the idea some time ago, the notion that escape velocity could be greater than the speed of light. Modern physicists and astronomers have a somewhat different idea for a black hole, involving the curvature of space.

Let us dimensionally reduce the curvature of space by two dimensions so we can illustrate three-space as a straight or curved line. The effect of a gravitational field on space near an object is illustrated in Fig. 7-9. At A, the effect is shown for a weak gravitational field. At B, the effect is shown for a stronger field; at C, for a very powerful gravitational source. These drawings are greatly exaggerated with respect to the effects produced by the planets or the sun (a true-scale drawing for these objects would have space looking like a straight line, the curvature imperceptible). I have

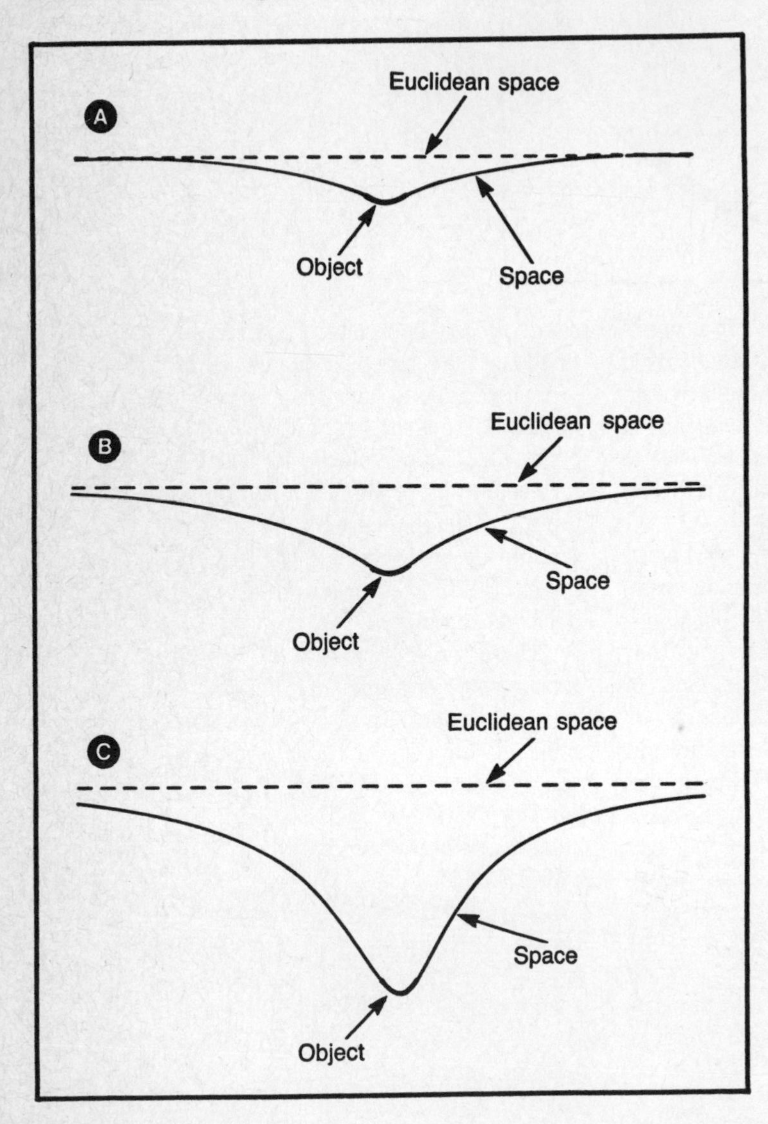

Fig. 7-9. Examples of the curvature of space in the vicinity of an object having a gravitational field. Examples A, B, and C show progressively more intense gravitational fields.

never heard of a name for this curvature, which in reality is shaped like a four-dimensional funnel, so let's make one up: let's call this curvature a ngaldi formation. That's an appropriately weird-sounding word for such a bizarre phenomenon as this.

Every object in space has a ngaldi around it. The sun has a big one; the planets have smaller ones. Your body has one. Even atoms and their constituent particles have ngaldis around them. In theory the effect of the curvature exists at any distance from any object. Though it be miniscule, the ngaldi effect for a proton, for example, has an effect on space a million light years away!

When a star reaches its dying stages, it contracts into a cold, dark ball of incredibly dense material. The gravitational field around such an object is extremely intense, and the ngaldi quite pronounced. When our own sun dies, it is believed it will have about the same mass as now, but with the diameter of our own Earth. It will have a pronounced ngaldi. Larger stars will contract to even more dense states. There is evidence to show that, if a star gets dense enough as it collapses upon itself, all the electrons in all of its atoms will be driven into the nuclei, the protons and electrons combining to form neutrons. The neutrons, along with the neutrons already present in the atomic nuclei, will be squeezed together like a mass of warm chocolate candies, forming one immense neutron ball. This object would be unimaginably dense and have an extremely deep ngaldi. A teaspoonful of the material of a neutron star would weigh thousands of tons. If you were to be on the surface of such an object, your body would immediately be assimilated into the neutron ooze and become part of the neutron star.

How much farther can this process go? This is the apparent paradox: there appears to be no limit. A neutron star, if massive enough, can, according to calculations made by astrophysicists, shrink down to a geometric point of infinite density. When it reaches a certain radial size, known as the *Schwarzchild radius* or *gravitational radius*, the ngaldi becomes infinitely deep (Fig. 7-10). The object literally disappears from the universe as we know it. Every object in the universe has a theoretical gravitational radius. For the sun, it is about 2.9 kilometers. For the earth it is about ½ centimeter. For your body it is on the order of atomic size. But even the tiniest particle has a gravitational radius.

From Fig. 7-10, we can see that escape from an object within its gravitational radius would be impossible. We would have to go infinitely far in order to get away. This is consistent with the notion that the escape velocity would be as great as, or more than, the speed of light, because even light cannot go infinitely far.

Do black holes really exist in the cosmos? Scientists aren't sure; we have never seen one come wandering into the solar system. Even a small one would produce gravitational effects that would disturb the orbits of the planets, and this has never happened. But recent observations indicate that such objects very possibly are out there, and may make up a significant part of the mass of our universe, matter that we cannot see, but which could have a profound impact on the evolution of the cosmos in the next few billion years.

Some astrophysicists have suggested that the entire universe has the correct size and density to be a black hole itself. The more massive an object, the larger its gravitational radius, and the less the density of the material when the object is that size. All the matter in the universe makes up a huge mass, and has a huge gravitational radius, and the material would not have to be very dense in order for it to be a black hole. In fact the density would be very low.

Imagine that the whole universe is a black hole! This is a possibility. Then it is finite, but we cannot escape from it. This is consistent with the notion that our three-dimensional space is the surface of a great four-sphere. If you were to travel far enough in one direction you would return to your starting place from the other direction, billions of years later.

Suppose further that the primary or fundamental particle—that elusive thing for which physicists keep searching—is in fact a black hole of miniscule size! Then the whole universe is one large black hole made up of myriad little ones. Carl Sagan, the

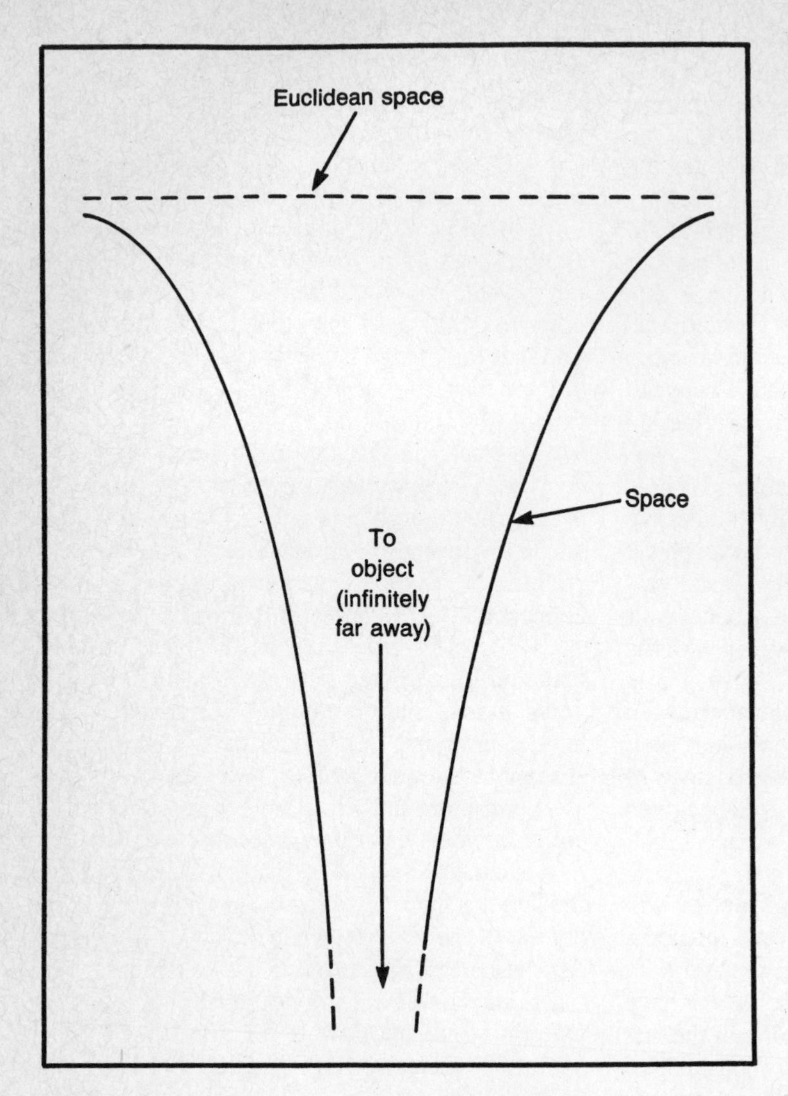

Fig. 7-10. A black hole. The object has reached such a density that the ngaldi is infinitely deep, space being stretched infinitely out of shape.

famous astrophysicist and author of many books on the subject, makes a suggestion in his book *Cosmos* that is somewhat along these lines. Perhaps our whole universe is but a primary particle in some greater universe, and every primary particle in our cosmos is a universe unto itself. This progression might go on infinitely into the large, and also into the small. Could this be? We don't know and probably never will.

Is all creation just a single point of zero size, with infinitely many dimensions, made up of black holes in infinite series large and small, with time never beginning nor ending? It wouldn't surprise me. Would it surprise you?

Appendix

Answers to problems in Chapter 1 involving Figs. 1-14, 1-15, 1-16, and 1-17, are shown here. These are examples; other solutions may exist.

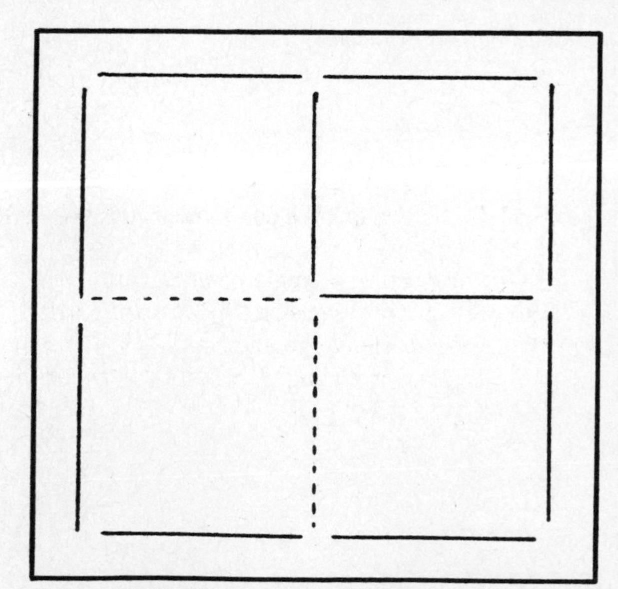

Fig. A-14. Remove two sticks, leaving two squares without having any sticks not part of a square.

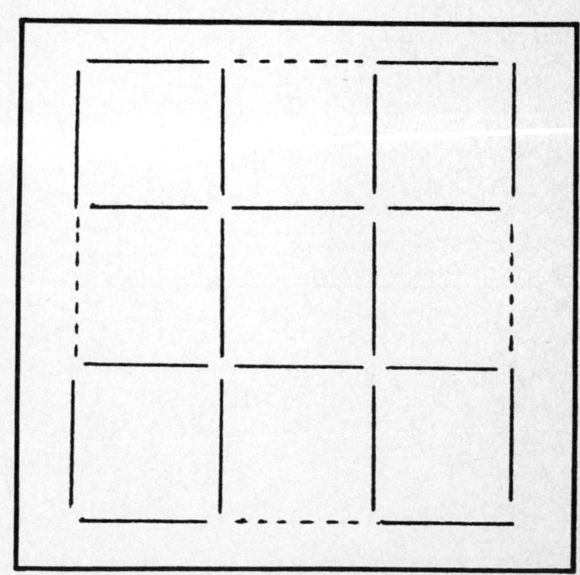

Fig. A-15. Remove four sticks to obtain five squares, without having any sticks not part of a square.

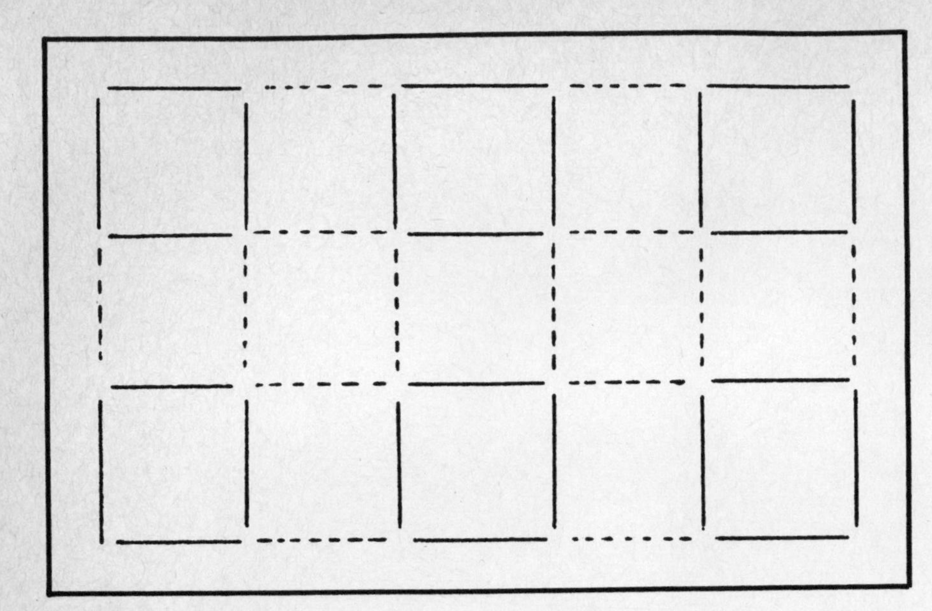

Fig. A-16. Remove 14 sticks, leaving six identical squares. Every stick remaining must form part of a square.

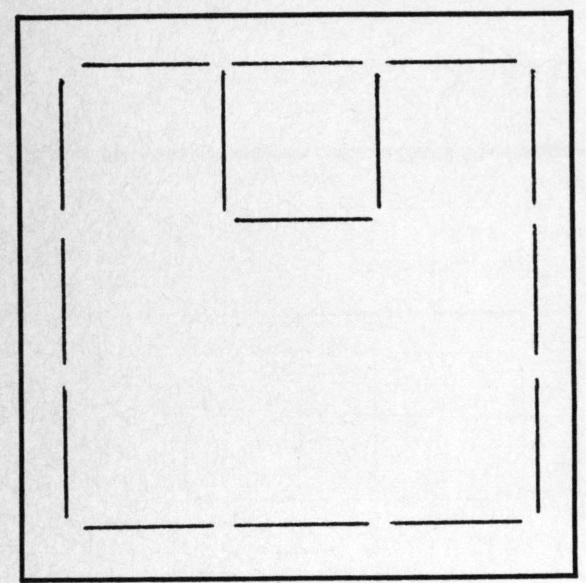

Fig. A-17. Move three of these sticks to get two squares. All sticks must form part of a square.

Index